PRENTICE R. GOODWIN

# digital tape drives

## DATA FREEWAYS INTO COMPUTERS

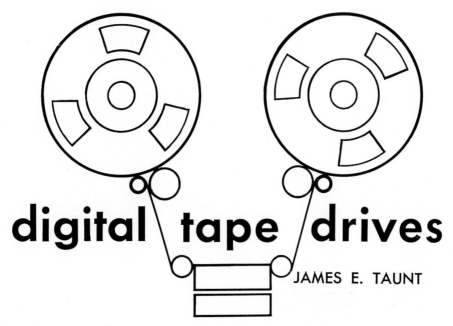

# digital tape drives

JAMES E. TAUNT

## DATA FREEWAYS INTO COMPUTERS

THE BUSINESS PRESS
Elmhurst, Illinois, U.S.A.
1965

# digital    tape    drives

DATA FREEWAYS INTO COMPUTERS

Copyright © 1965 by

O. A. Business Publications, Inc.

Printed in the United States of America

Library of Congress Catalog Card Number: 65-19526

**J. M. J.**

●

TO THE BEST

COMPUTER SYSTEMS I KNOW

**GRACE, MARTA, LINDA, AND MOTHER**

●

# INTRODUCTION

This book is intended for people associated with digital computers—operators, programmers, analysts, managers and consultants. It is not written in the technical language that best serves an engineer. Of course, technical terms must be used in a work of this sort, but wherever possible, they have been explained. Also, when dealing with the mathematics of energy, liberties have been taken with the numbers game. Mathematicians could poke holes in the presentations, since for reasons of clarity certain short cuts have been taken and extensive proofs omitted.

This is a book for individuals who want to learn about *DIGITAL TAPE DRIVES*. Throughout the book, I make reference to the cost of the computer, which I have arbitrarily set at $100 per hour. Some computers cost more, some less than this figure. If the reader has a particular computer in mind that has a different cost per hour, he can easily calculate his own cost.

Unfortunately, the industry has grown up with a number of different terms meaning the same thing. *Write enable, file protect, write inhibit,* are all the plastic rings that fit in the back of the tape reel. *Tape transport, tape unite, tape drive,* are all the mechanisms which move tape over the head. And we have *inter-record gaps*, which fit between record blocks on tape. Our terms are not uniform or consistent. I plead guilty to not doing much to help the situation. In this work I have tried to be uniform in the use of the terms. But, at times I talk about blocking records on tape, writing a block, and then the diagrams have *record size* for the base. On this subject, I took the coward's way out. I have used the words that seem most common in usage. The American Standards Association (ASA) is working on standardization of terms.

Many manufacturers have been very kind in furnishing pictures of their product. Ampex, Potter, and Midwestern Instruments also sent background information. The Pyrol Company of France gave permission to use any data from their book "High Performance Tapes." Credits and quotations have been cited as they appear in the book. The reader will note that there are some manufacturers whose products are not illustrated. There are three reasons for this. First, my ignorance of the manufacturer's product. I may have thought that the particular company purchased their drives from a vendor, rather than making their own. Second, some manufacturers did not choose to contribute any material. Finally, I may have asked for the pictures too late in the writing cycle. Some manufacturers seemed to be tied up in the mailing and approval cycle so that their pictures did not arrive on time. Except for the above three reasons, nothing should be inferred about a manufacturer who does not have a picture in this book.

In most introductions one finds the sentence "So many people have contributed to this work that it is impossible to thank them all but . . ." Believe me, I have read through that sentence many times and said to myself, "Cut out the baloney, what have you got to say?" You can be sure that from now on I will read through that standard sentence with much more understanding. When people learned that I was writing a book, their hearts and minds opened up with all sorts of good suggestions and help. A ten-second suggestion was sometimes more valuable than sixteen hours' work. But I would like to list those people who contributed a substantial amount of time to this work. Marcy Mitchell and Liz Pheffier did my typing. Ray Shanahan gave me direction and chased down releases and permissions at GE. Jack Webb gave me repeated encouragement when I was ready to quit. No man is alone in the modern world; he depends on the help of others. I depended on these people and others.

# contents

**Chapter**

# 1 introduction to tape drives

FOR AS LONG AS MAN HAS THOUGHT about the design of computers, he has also thought about input-output devices. Von Neuman wrote about the tape drive, "It must be fast enough so that a large percentage of the total solution time is not spent in getting data into and out of this medium and achieving the desired positioning on it. If this condition is not reasonably well met, the advantages of high electronic speeds of the machine will be largely lost." ( Quoted by permission of *Datamation.*)

Have we lost the advantage of the high speed computers? It is pretty evident that the advantages have not been lost. But how have the tape drives been able to keep up with the electronic development? And, can the development of tape drives continue to keep up with the micro-miniature circuits and other electronics of the future? This book is about tape drives. It explains how tape drives keep up with present computers, and how they will continue to do so. Various techniques of tape drives are compared to demonstrate the advantages of each individual technique and to give a better perspective on the system.

## why do we use tape drives?

The term *tape drive* can be interpreted to mean *magnetic digital tape transports*. Tape drive is shorter, and is the term used by the operators. There are other input-output devices on a computer. Some of these devices are as fast as a tape drive; some hold as much information as a tape drive; some can even read and write. Why are tape drives still with us?

To answer the question, let's take a brief look at each one of the other devices. The oldest media of input-output is the punch card. The card reader and card punch were on the first commercial computer. The punch card has the wonderful advantage of being a unit record. That means that one card has the information for one person, one item, or one thing. When you have a punch card, you don't have someone else's record, and he doesn't have your record. This is a necessary advantage in paychecks and utility bills. A punched card bill applies to one and only one thing. Besides the advantage of being a unit record, the punch card has other advantages. A card is cheap, durable and permanent—it is difficult to unpunch a card. Because the card is so durable, it can be read reasonably fast.

1

## 2 digital tape drives

While a card can be read fast—up to 25 cards a second or 4 KC—it cannot be punched fast. Three hundred and fifty cards a minute is about as fast as cards can be punched. (350 CPM gives 5.8 cards per second or 0.9 KC.) So if anyone is planning to use punched cards as the principal input-output media for a computer, the computer must be slow, to match card speed.

Printed characters is another fine media for input-output. They are in a common language. Anyone can step up the printer and read what the results are. This is something that can't be done with punched cards or magnetic tape. The output from a printer is fairly fast: 1,000 to 1,500 lines per minute (17 to 25 lines a second for 2.7 to 4.0 KC). But how does one get printed information back into the computer? There are characters readers, but these are slow and expensive. (0.5KC. for $3,000/month) The printed character doesn't fit the need for fast input-output.

Next is paper tape. This is an old medium too. It is almost as old as the telegraph. And paper tape can be read reasonably fast—2 KC. But it can be punched only at 150 characters per second (0.15 KC.) Paper tape is used by a number of small computers as the primary input-output. Other media has better input-output speeds, but paper tape has an important advantage. Its input-output equipment is well developed and inexpensive. Also, there are key-driven typewriters which will punch paper tape. However, only small or specialized computers can justify paper tape as the primary input-output.

By now it is obvious that magnetic devices must be utilized to get the high-transfer speeds needed. A magnetic disk is an excellent device. A disk is fast and reliable. (Input-output speeds up to 180 KC.)

The input and output speeds are both fast. Indeed there are a number of computers that use the disk as the principal input-output device. But there are not very many of these. Why? Because we cannot store enough information on a disk. If a disk file contains 280 million characters, it is a big file. If we were able to write to it at its peak rate constantly, it would take 1,600 seconds or a little under a half hour to fill the disk. Then what would we do for storage? A disk file has limited storage.

By pointing out all the problems with various devices, I hope to demonstrate what is needed in a primary input-output device. The device must:

1. *Be fast Input, many KC.*
2. *Be fast Output, many KC.*
3. *Have huge storage, many days' work.*

Some of the devices listed have some of these characteristics, but none of them have them all. Let's review. Punched cards are slow input-output but can store many days' work. The printed character is fairly fast as an output. It is able to store many days' work. But its input ability is too slow. Magnetic disks has fast input/output speeds, but it can store only a few hours' work, not days'.

In most applications, none of the above devices have the characteristics needed in a primary input-output device. In some special applications, where all the characteristics are not required, each of these devices has found a place in computer work. Punch cards and paper tape are primary input and output on slow-speed machines. Paper tape is an output media where the output is to be used directly on numeric control machine tools. The information must be in the described media. Some computers which switch repetitive information have been able to use the magnetic disk as the primary input-output device. Inquiries are constantly being received. Can we reserve seat number xx on plane yy? The answer is switched back, yes or no. The actual data transfer rates on this type of computer does not have to be very high. What is needed is low access time to any record.

Only one device supplies all the characteristics of a primary input-output device—the tape drive.

Tape drives are:

1. *Fast input, 240 KC and faster.*
2. *Fast output, 240 KC and faster.*
3. *Good storage, no practical limit to amount of storage.*

Tape drives are the primary input-output devices on every large scale digital computers. Since tape drives are so important to the computer industry, let's talk about them. Much can be said.

## this book is written because

A better understanding of tape drives will enable us to better utilize them, be more aware of what can be done with them, and increase our results. Also, a better understanding will allow us to make adequate compensations for their shortcomings.

The literature is indicating that the glamor is just about worn off the computer. Managers, operators, programmers, and engineers are looking at computers for what they have been all along—machines to relieve men's minds of the routine calculations, machines to do the nonimaginative work. The steam engine relieved men's hands. Computers are relieving men's minds. Therefore, it behooves us to get the most out of the machines we have. No one can get the most out of a computer unless he really understands its input-output devices—the tape drives.

## elements of a tape drive

There are five principle elements in a tape drive. Each one is dependent on the other four. The five elements are:

1. *Reel storage and drive system.*
2. *Buffer tape storage system (vacuum columns, dancer arms or scramble bins)*
3. *Capstan drive system*
4. *Head and tape sensing elements*
5. *Electronic control logic*

Finally, there is another element in transport design which is not a part of the design at all. That is the magnetic tape itself. The limitations of the tape are directly transmitted to the drive and vice versa. Each of the elements of the drive will be discussed in more detail.

For the most practical tape drives, all the elements described above are present. However, if the performance of any one of the elements is reduced to a low level compared to presently accepted standards, it is possible that one or more of the other elements may disappear. For example, most tape drives move at 36 to 150 ips (inches per second) and start and stop in 3 to 10 MS (milliseconds) after receipt of a command. This performance dictates a "slack loop of tape" between the head and the reels. If a slack loop is not present, the inertia of the reels and the rapid acceleration of the tape by the capstan will break the tape. If the speed of the tape is reduced to two inches per second (IPS), or start time is made 200 MS, the "slack loop of tape" may not be needed. The stretch of the tape becomes the storage. It is well to

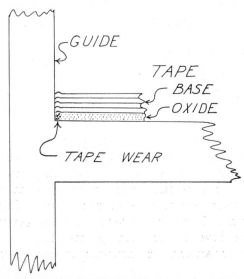

**Fig. 1**—GUIDES WEARING MAGNETIC TAPE. This picture shows how the guiding system on a particular drive wore the oxide off the edge of the tape. Very high guiding pressure was used on the tape. The base material compressed and exposed the oxide to the wearing action of the guides.

keep in mind that the comments in this book refer to the most generally accepted standards. A tape drive with greatly reduced performance does not necessarily have all the elements described here.

## the tape media

The tape itself requires consideration. Any tape drive requires certain characteristics of the magnetic tape. The tolerance on the tape width cannot be too great, or guiding is impossible; the tape must have certain tensil strength, or capstan acceleration is impossible; and so forth. As the magnetic tape properties have improved, transport design has changed to accommodate the new characteristics. In at least one case, the transports were changed to prevent the new improved tape characteristics from doing damage to the transport.

This example is given to illustrate the effects of one element on the others. A particular transport used stainless steel guides on the tape. In the days of only soft binder oxide tape these guides were removing oxide from the edge of the tape (Fig. 1). However, as tape manufacturers improved their binder and began to market hard binder tape, the

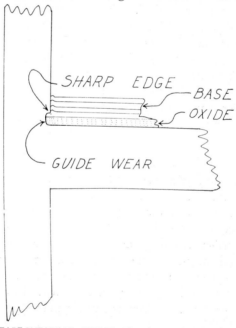

**Fig. 2—MAGNETIC TAPE WEARING GUIDES.** This shows what happened to the guides in Fig. 1 after hard binder tape was developed. The base material compressed as before, but this time the oxide wore the guides. This developed a very sharp edge in the guides which sheared off long threads of base material. These threads of base material got between the read head and the oxide and caused errors.

guides were worn before they could remove the oxide (Fig. 2). This action left the stainless steel guides with a razor sharp edge. This sharp edge in turn shaved off the edge of all the rest of the tape that passed over the guide. The improved magnetic tape had damaged the machine guides and then the machine guides damaged the remainder of the tape.

This sort of change and improvement is part of the price paid for progress. Accurate field reporting with perceptive engineering is the answer to keeping the effects of these problems to a minimum.

## caution

One note of caution to the reader—the work around a computer is very satisfying and challenging, and people who operate, program, maintain, or design computer equipment become very involved in their work. People are emotional, and some of the observations made are based more on emotion than on fact. I would therefore suggest that the reader consider the merits of the following presentation from the logic or lack of logic rather than from the point of view, "The XYZ drive had that feature and it never worked." The success or failure of any particular design on any tape drive is involved with many factors. Is the design good? Is it manufactured well? Is adequate maintenance available? Is the design being pushed beyond its original intended limits? Is some other tape drive trouble being reflected into the particular design being questioned? The analysis and description of a tape drive may require strict control of emotions which may have been built up over a hot computer at 2:00 AM some Sunday morning.

## in summary

High-speed computers need fast input-output devices. They also need very large amounts of data storage. There are a number of special computers which do not follow these requirements, but these cannot be described as general purpose computers. At the present time the only device which satisfies all the needs of a high-speed computer for input-output is a digital magnetic tape transport, a tape drive. A tape drive has five separate elements which determine its performance. The remainder of this book will deal with each of these elements. In addition, other areas of interest will be discussed and explained.

## CHAPTER 1. Questions

1. What are the requirements for the primary input/output devices on a digital computer?
2. Compare punched cards, paper tape, disk, printed information and magnetic tape against the above requirements.
3. What are the five divisions of a tape drive?

# 2 reels

THE REELS ARE THE PART OF A TAPE DRIVE that everybody sees—the big colored disks that turn first one way and then the other. But what causes the big disk to turn one way and then the other? This chapter will deal with the 'what,' not the 'why,' of turning tape reels. This chapter will describe what is needed to turn, stop, and reverse the reels. The next chapter will describe the 'why,' the logic which causes the reels to go this way, then that way.

The only 'why' on reel turning that will be dealt with in this chapter is, "Why are reel systems important?" If we think about it a bit, it seems obvious that there is no better way of storing a large amount of tape than winding it on a reel. Other materials that have to be stored are wrapped on spools—newsprint, wrapping paper, sheet steel, and cloth—in fact almost any material which is large in two directions and small in the third. And the only way to get the material off is to turn the spool. You can't pull the material out of the center like string, because it will twist. (No one minds that string twists as it is pulled out.) Therefore, in order to get tape off a reel, we have to turn the reel. And of course we have to stop the reel.

## tape drives are different

This may not seem like a very challenging job. And it isn't, on analog recorders. Home tape recorders, instrumentation recorders, and video tape recorders are able to turn the reel with very little trouble. But the problem is different on a digital tape drive. The big difference is frequency. On a home tape recorder, the reel is started and it continues to run until we have recorded a song or speech, or until it is played back. An instrumentation recorder will start up and record the results of a two or three-minute test. And of course the video tape recorder never stops until the one-minute commercial is completed. Even an office dictating tape recorder doesn't have to start and stop more often than every four or five seconds. The frequency of start and stop on the above devices is measured in minutes or seconds. The frequency of start and stop on a digital tape recorder is measured in hundreds of milliseconds (MS) at best, and may be measured in tens of milliseconds. So the reels on a digital tape drive must start and stop five or fifty times a second. That is why the turning and stopping of a reel of tape is a challenging job on a digital tape drive. It is a matter of frequency.

## how many start-stops per minute?

The controlling factor on how fast a reel of tape has to be started and stopped is the size of the buffer storage. This will be dealt with in the next chapter. If the storage is very large, the reels can be started and stopped at a slow rate. Large buffers cost money. It becomes a choice between the cost of starting the reels faster and that of providing more buffer storage. For the present, we will assume that the buffer storage requires the reels to start and stop ten to twenty times a second.

## laws of nature

Let's talk about one of the laws of nature, conservation of energy. This law says that energy cannot be made or destroyed. Energy can only be converted into other forms. The atomic bomb combined the law of conservation of energy with the law of conservation of matter. But since we are not dealing with an atomic reaction in a tape drive we can use the definitions stated above, "Energy cannot be destroyed."

Just what is energy? When we lift a book off a table, we are putting potential energy into the book. We did work to lift the book. If we throw the book across the room, we put kinetic energy into the book. The work we did to get the book moving was kinetic energy. But what happens when the book hits the floor? The kinetic energy comes out. Where does it go? The kinetic energy comes out of the book as heat when the book slides on the floor.

Rub your fingers on the palm of your hand, very rapdily. Feel the heat? This is the energy of motion being transformed into heat. When the book slid on the floor, the energy of motion was transformed into heat. Technically, the kinetic energy (KE) was converted into heat energy. The kinetic energy in a spinning reel of tape also turns to heat. Every time a reel of tape is stopped, something else receives the energy of motion as heat. If we stop a reel of tape many times a second, something gets hot. This chapter deals with the problems of putting energy into the reel and taking it out.

The problem of reel control boils down to putting kinetic energy into the reels or taking kinetic energy out. Since the tape buffer storage system is not infinitely large, there is a time limit on how fast this can be done. Consequently, power as well as energy is involved.

The only difference between power and energy is time. If a Ford car pulls a trailer full of rocks up a hill, the Ford has put energy into the rock. The Ford has done work to lift the rocks up a hill. If a Volkswagen pulls the same rocks up the same hill, it has done the same amount of work. The VW has put the same energy into the rocks. But the Ford pulled the rocks up the hill much faster than the VW would. The Ford used more power, but it gave the rocks the same energy. The rate of energy flow is power.

The rate at which a reel of tape must be started or stopped determines the power requirements. No matter what the rate is, the energy in the reel is the same. Power depends on time, energy does not.

## energy switches or clutches

Kinetic energy is put into a reel through a clutch. This clutch may be an electromagnetic friction clutch, magnetic clutch, AC motor, or DC motor. For the purpose of this chapter, all these elements are lumped into one term, *clutch*.

All the energy in the reel must be taken out through a brake. The brake may be a friction brake, magnetic brake, AC motor or DC motor. The brake may be separated from the clutch or it may be the same unit. As mentioned previously, there is a time limit on how fast the energy can be put into the reel and taken out. For a practical tape drive, this time ranges between 10 and 250 milliseconds. So the clutch must have a power rating.

## heat problems

Before we can appreciate reel design, we must have a feel for the heat problem in the reel clutch. Once we have this feel, we can see why computers use IBM type reels instead of NAB. We can also see why power switching is important, and why some drives have a brake as well as a motor. So let's get into the heat problem.

I have already described the law of conservation of energy. Heat, motion energy, and potential or height energy have been shown to be the same. There is one other concept that will help. This is the idea of a demon. The famous scientist, Maxwell, used the most celebrated demon to analyze a heat problem. A demon is a little fellow who will go anywhere and report exacly what he sees. My demon is a little fellow who will go anywhere. He reports exactly what he sees. And he can see any of nature's laws in action. This demon never gets dizzy riding on motor shafts or anything like that. The demon is a quick, accurate, technical reporter.

## heat flow going from one speed to zero (1 S to 0 S)

For example, suppose that we have a reel of tape spinning at speed 1 S. The reel has energy of motion. Let us call this energy of motion 1 KE. Let's put our demon on the reel to observe. We now engage a clutch (brake) to stop the reel. We know from the example of the book that all the motion energy 1 KE, must be removed as heat 1 H. The little demon is riding on the reel (Fig. 3). From his vantage point it looks as if everybody else is turning and he is standing still. As the clutch brake

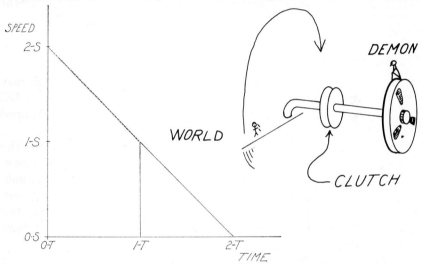

**Fig. 3**—DEMON VIEWS THE WORLD TURNING AT 1-S. As the demon sits on the reel of tape, it appears to him that the world is turning and he is standing still. After a time, when the clutch is engaged, the world slows down and comes to a stop. The energy difference between the world and the reel comes out as heat in the clutch. The diagram shows what happens to the speed of the reel. At time 1-T the reel is turning at a speed of 1-S. At time 2-T, the reel is stopped.

is applied it appears to the demon that there is grinding and sliding motion between his reel and the rest of the world. The world slows down, and he sees an amount of heat, 1 H, equal to the motion energy of the reels 1 KE. From the outside world, we see the same laws of nature as the demon. A reel of tape was turning, a clutch (brake) was engaged, and the motion energy 1 KE was used up as heat 1 H. To the demon it appeared that the world slowed down to his speed. To us it appeared that the reel slowed down to the world. But, both of us saw the same heat generated, 1 H from the motion energy 1 KE.

## heat 2 S to -0 S

Now suppose that the reel is turning at twice the speed, 2S. What will the demon see? The entire operation will be repeated with different amounts of energy being used. It happens that the energy of motion is proportional to the square of the speed. This means that if the reel speed is twice, the energy is four times. So the energy in the reels is 4x1 KE or 4 KE. And the heat energy that the demon must see in the clutch brake will be 4x1 H or 4 H. Let's get a blow-by-blow description of the demon's ride.

The demon is riding the reel, which we know is turning at twice its former speed. The demon sees the world turning at twice the previous speed. The world starts to slow down. When the world has slowed down to a speed of 1 S, what has happened, and what is left? We know what is left. From here on it is a repetition of the previous example. The demon is going to see the world come to a halt. And he is going to see heat generated in the amount of 1 H, equal to motion energy of 1 KE. But this operation started from a motion energy of 4 KE. Therefore, in going from a speed of 2 S to one of 1 S, the demon saw 3 H of heat generated.

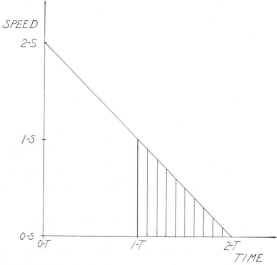

**Fig. 4—SPEED TIME PLOT FROM 2-S.** The demon sees the same picture as he saw in Fig. 3. However, the energy diagram is bigger. The line starts at twice the speed and lasts for twice as long. The area under the curve, energy, is four times.

The demon changed speeds by 1 S and saw 3 H units of heat generated. The amount of heat that is generated is dependent on the speed change as well as on the difference in speed between the reel and the world. Notice in Figure 4 that the cross-hatched section can be filled in by the diagram in Figure 3. The important point here is that the amount of energy converted into heat is dependent on the speed change of the reels as well as the speed difference between the clutch and the reel. When the reels went from speed 2 S to 1 S, 3x1 H units of heat were converted. When the reels went from speed 1 S to 0 S, 1 H units of heat were converted. Reel speed change and reel clutch speed difference are the controlling factors.

## mathematics of heat flow

This book is not intended as a mathematical treatment of clutches. But it will add to our understanding of the reel problem to use some simple mathematics on the previous curves. The kinetic energy (KE) in the reel is equal to the inertia of the reel (I) times the square of the velocity (S). $KE = I S^2$. The energy is also equal to the torque, or braking force (t), times the speed of the reel (S), times the time (T). $KE = t S T$. Just to make things simple, let's give our observant demon a switch. Let's tell the demon to operate the switch so that the braking torque is a constant. Since he is a good little demon, he will do this for us. This constant torque makes the energy in the reel a square function of time. The speed of the reel is then a straight-line function of time $IS^2 = KE = tST$ or $IS = tT$ (t is held constant by the demon). During the braking action, the speed of the reel will decrease linearly with time. And, since the energy in the reel is equal to the constant torque times the speed times time, ($KE = t S T$), the area under the curve represents the energy removed from the reel.

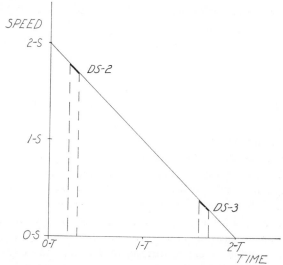

**Fig. 5—SPEED TIME PLOT FROM 2-S IN SMALL PIECES.** This diagram shows how the area under a small speed change can be different. DS-2 is the same change as DS-3. However, because DS-2 takes place at a much higher speed, the area under DS-2 is much greater than under DS-3. Hence, the heat loss under DS-2 is much greater than under DS-3.

Armed with these mathematical tools, let's plot the speed time curve for 2 S to 0 S again. But this time let's ask the demon to signal us for two small speed changes DS 2 and DS 3 near the beginning and end of the action. Both these speed changes are small and equal. These are plotted in Figure 5. The area under DS 2 is much greater than the area under DS 3. This re-emphasizes the important point. The energy used in heating the clutch is as much dependent on the change of speed as it is on the difference between speeds.

In a previous example we check the energy at 2 S, 1 S and 0 S. In this example we checked the energy after two small speed changes DS. Both cases demonstrate that the energy lost in the clutch is a function of speed change and the difference in speed between the reel and the clutch face.

The energy in the system can be tabulated in the following manner:

## Table I.

| Location of Energy | 2 S Reel Speed | 1 S Reel Speed | 0 S Reel Speed |
|--------------------|----------------|----------------|----------------|
| Reel | 4 KE | 1 KE | 0 KE |
| Clutch | 0 H | 3 H | 4 H |
| Totals | 4 | 4 | 4 |

### heat 1 S TO — 1 S

Since our demon is doing so well for us, let's keep him working. This time, let's have the reel turn at speed S. But the clutch is not standing still. Let the clutch be turning a speed of minus S ( —S ), in the opposite direction to the reel. Now we will give the demon the torque control switch and have him tell us what he sees.

Before braking begins, he is going to see the world turning at 1 S as he has seen it in previous examples. But this time the clutch is turning twice as fast as the world is turning ( Fig. 6 ). Now the clutch engages. The demon sees the same grinding and friction that he saw when the reel was turning 2 S. For the grinding and scraping between the reel and the clutch is not dependent on the speed of the world. The action is dependent on the difference in speed between the demon and reel and the clutch face. The demon saw the clutch turning at a speed of 2 S just as he did for Figure 4, and therefore he sees the same energy lost in heat as he saw in Figure 4. (We know that the clutch is not turning at 2 S but the reel is turning at 1 S and the clutch is turning at —1 S.) What the demon sees is not dependent on our knowledge, but only what he sees. And what he sees is theoretically and mathematically correct. What he is seeing is true and actual heat flow.

When the reel has been slowed down to a stop, as we see it, what does the demon see? The demon sees that the world has stopped spinning, and has been slowed down to a stop also. But the clutch brake is spinning at the speed that the world was when he started this action —1 S. The demon keeps his torque switch on and continues the braking action. To the demon the situation looks like example two, Figure 4. The demon is half-way through the braking ride from 2 S, 1 S to 0S. (World speed 1 S, 0 S to —1 S)

After a time the demon will see the clutch slow down and come to a stop with the reel. It is a little strange now, because the world is now turning in the opposite direction from what it was when he started out. Let's plot the demon's ride in Figure 6. The curve looks like the curve in Figure 4. The only difference is that the zero speed for the world is at speed S. And indeed this is the only difference to the demon. The heat generated in the clutch is the same as it was for braking from 2 S. This brings home the point again, that the heat lost in the clutch is as dependent on the speed change as on the speed difference between the reel and the clutch.

There is one other difference between the examples. Table II on page 16 will point it out.

In the first example, it was easy to keep track of the energy. The

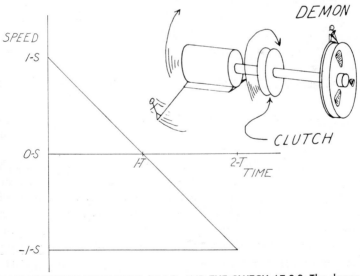

**Fig. 6**—DEMON VIEWS THE WORLD AT 1-S, AND THE CLUTCH AT 2-S. The demon riding the reel sees that the world is turning at 1-S. This means to us that he is turning at 1-S. But, he also sees the clutch turning at 2-S. The heat loss that is observed is dependent on the speed difference between him and the clutch. A motor turns the clutch at 2-S. The speed time plot is very similar to Fig. 4. One minor difference is the 0-S is half way thru the braking action. When considering the heat loss in the clutch, this difference is not significant.

## Table II.

| Location of Energy | Start | Half-way thru | End |
|---|---|---|---|
| Reel Fig. 4<br>2 S to 0 S | 4 KE | 1 KE | 0 KE |
| Reel Fig. 6<br>+1 S to −1 S | 1 KE | 0 KE | 1 KE |
| Clutch—both cases | O H | 3 H | 4 H |

total energy in the system is equal to four, (4KE, OH) (1KE, 3H) (OKE, 4 H).

But in the second example, the number doesn't balance out. 1 KE, 0 H), (0 KE, 3 H), (1 KE, 4 H). What happened, and where did the energy come from? The extra energy came from a motor that must be driving the clutch in the reverse direction. The demon sees 4 H heat lost in the clutch as the reel changes speed from 1 S to 0 S to −1 S. The reel tended to stop the spinning clutch. But the motor which is driving the clutch kept putting energy into the system to keep the clutch turning at −1 S. The table could be restated as follows:

## Table III.

| Location of Energy | Start | Half-way thru | End |
|---|---|---|---|
| 1st CASE—Figure 4 (2 S—O S) | | | |
| Reel | 4 KE | 1 KE | 0 KE |
| Clutch | 0 H | 3 H | 4 H |
| Energy to clutch | 0 | 0 | 0 |
| Total | 4 | 4 | 4 |
| 2nd CASE—Figure 6 (1 S— (−1 S)) | | | |
| Reel | 1 KE | 0 KE | 1 KE |
| Clutch | 0 H | 3 H | 4 H |
| Energy available to clutch | 4 | 2 | 0 |
| Total | 5 | 5 | 5 |

So the law of conservation of energy is still with us. When applying the law, we have to consider inputs and outputs from all sources.

Notice in Case 2 that 1 H units of heat are lost in the clutch when the reel is accelerated from 0 S to −1 S. 1 KE was put into the reel, and 1 H was lost in the clutch. The same amount of energy was lost in the clutch accelerating the reel 1 S as is lost stopping the reel 1 S. Here is a fundamental point. It doesn't matter whether the reel is accelerating or decelerating, the heat loss in the clutch is the same. The heat loss in the clutch is only dependent on the speed difference and the speed change of the reel. The heat loss is independent of the direction of energy flow.

## heat 2 S to 1 S

One more example of heat loss during clutching is to be considered, in order to round out the discussion of heat lost in clutching. This example does not have much application in tape drives but it is interesting. Consider the reel turning at 2 S, and the clutch turning in the same direction at 1 S. What is the heat loss, and where does all the energy go?

Let's wake up the little demon, put him on the reel, and start a test. The demon sees the world turning at 2 S, but the clutch is turning at 1 S. The demon sees the clutch engage, he controls his torque switch for uniform torque, and observes the same heat loss that he always sees. The reel changed speed 1 S, with a difference of speed of 1 S. The demon sees a heat loss of 1 H.

He also sees something different. The reel was turning at 2 S, so it had 4 KE units of kinetic energy. After the clutching the reel turned at 1 S, and had 1 KE unit of kinetic energy. What happend to all the difference? It is an opposite effect from that of the last experiment. The reel tended to speed up the clutch, and the motor driving the clutch had to absorb energy to keep the speed down. The table would look like this:

### Table IV.

| Location of Energy | Start | Ending |
|---|---|---|
| Reel | 4 KE | 1 KE |
| Clutch | 0 H | 1 H |
| Energy into drive Motor (which acted as generator) | 0 | 2 |
| | 4 | 4 |

The law of conservation of energy still holds up. See Figure 7 (page 18) for energy plot of the above case. But this time we get the startling condition of slowing the reels down and getting some of the energy back. It is theoretically possible to slow down a reel and get energy back.

## summary of heat loss

The heat loss in a clutch is dependent on the reel to clutch speed difference and the reel speed change. The heat loss is independent of the world to clutch speed, or world to reel speed.

In practice this means that when 1 KE of energy is put into a reel to accelerate it to operating speed, 1 H of energy is lost in the clutch as heat. When the 1 KE is taken out of the reel to stop the reel, a second 1 H of heat is developed. For every 1 KE of energy put into the reel, 2 H of energy is lost in the clutch system, 1 H putting energy into the reel, and 1 H taking energy out of the reel. More than this

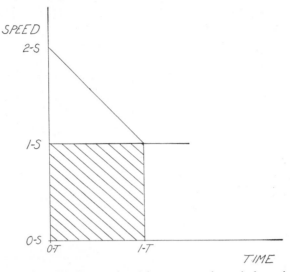

**Fig. 7—MOTOR SLOWS REEL.** This is a plot of the energy and speed of a reel when a motor is used to slow the reel. The clear area is heat loss in the clutch. The shaded area is energy put into the electric motor. This energy is converted into electricity and put out on the lines. The motor is acting as a generator during the braking action.

minimum amount of heat will be dissipated in the clutch if the clutch is not running at the terminal speed of the reel. Remember, 4 H of energy were lost in the clutch taking 1 KE of energy out of the reel when the clutch turned at —1 S rather than 0 S. Generally, three or four times as much energy is lost in the clutch as heat as is put into the reel to accelerate it to operating speed.

## heatless reel drive

There is one way that the kinetic energy can be taken out of the reel without developing heat loss. This can be done with the a torsion spring, and a brake. Let us assume that we have a torsion spring with the reels at 1 S speed. See Figure 8 for the demon's view. Both clutch **A** and clutch **B** are brakes. Clutch **A** is used to stop the tail end of the spring and clutch **B** is used to stop the reel. In this experiment, we are going to engage clutch **A** to start the reel stopping and engage clutch **B** when the reel stops. The demon sees the world turning at speed 1 S. He then sees clutch **A** engage. Very little energy is lost in that clutching action. Very little of the spinning stopped with the clutching. The reel is slowing down, and the energy from the reel is going into the spring tension. When the reel stops, clutch **B** engages. But no energy is trans-

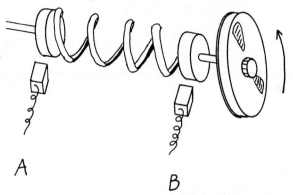

Fig. 8—REELS STOPPED WITH A SPRING. It is theoretically possible to stop a reel of tape with a spring. Clutch "A" engages to catch the tail of the spring. Because little mass is stopped, little energy is lost. Once Clutch "A" is engaged, the spring winds up and converts reel kinetic energy into spring tension energy. When the reel is stopped, Clutch "B" engages to hold the system.

ferred because there is no relative motion between the reel and the clutch. The Energy Table is:

## Table V.

| Location of Energy | Beginning | Ending |
|---|---|---|
| Reel | 1 KE | 0 KE |
| Clutch | 0 | 0 (A clutch has a small amount) |
| Spring | 0 | 1 |
| Total | 0 | 1 |

Therefore it is possible to build a reel drive system that doesn't waste any energy as heat. However, the mechanics of the torsion spring, sensing when the reels are stopped so that **B** clutch can be engaged, and making up for the small amount of energy lost in **A** clutch, have kept this reel drive system in the lab. Tape drive designers prefer to handle the heat problem than to handle the mechanism necessary to keep the spring wound up.

There is one other problem. If the reels are being stopped from 2 S, and at 1 S the reel has had to be re-accelerated, the reel motion will have to be taken down to 0 and then back up to 2 S.

## comparison of reel clutches

When a reel is stopped or slowed down by a clutch, some

motion energy is converted into heat energy or potential energy. Heat energy must be dissipated to the atmosphere. Potential energy (the spring, and motor generator examples) can be reused the next time the reel is accelerated.

This has been a very technical discussion of clutching and breaking actions. If you feel that you have a grasp—however slight—of the fundamentals, pat yourself on the back. I have met a number of engineers in more than one company who did not appreciate this problem. Do not hesitate to come back and review the tables to keep your status of "expert."

### dc motors clutches

There are various types of clutches used on reel drives. The most common one is the DC motor. More manufacturers use DC motors to start and stop the reels than any other clutching means.

The series DC motor has a speed torque curve like Figure 9. Two things have led to the predominate choice of a DC motor as the energy source for the reel drives. First, the motor has a high torque in the speed range of interest (450 to 900 revolutions per minute, rpm). Second, for

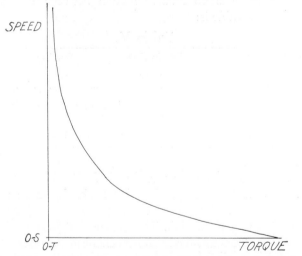

**Fig. 9**—SPEED TORQUE CURVE OF A 'DC' SERIES MOTOR. This curve describes the speed torque relationship of a series DC motor. When the motor is stopped the torque is maximum.

those systems that servo their reels, the shape of the speed torque curve makes the servo amplifier simpler. To servo the reels means to try to keep the reels turning at a speed just fast enough to supply the needs of capstan. In the technical definition of the word, all reels are servoed. Servo simply means to feed information from the output back to the input for control. As the term is used in the digital tape drive industry, "servo" means to increase the information flow from the output, so that the reel does not overspeed.

High torque for starting and easy servo control has led to the choice of DC motors. See examples in Figure 10.

**Fig. 10**—REAR VIEW OF A DIGITAL DRIVE USING DC REEL MOTORS. The two larger horizontal series DC motors turn the reels. Notice the flange mount to the frame for heat conduction. These motors are designed to withstand all the heat caused by starting and stopping. *Courtesy GE Computer Department.*

One might ask just what speed the motor is turning when clutching action taks place. Since DC motors do not have a synchronous speed, it is difficult—but not impossible—to determine. The clutch speed of a DC motor is the speed it would be turning with the applied voltage, and no load on the armature. In other words, if the applied voltage would turn the armature at 2 S with no load on the armature, the heat losses in the motor due to clutching can be figured from a speed of 2 S. Thus if a reel is accelerated to 1 S, 3 H units of heat went into the clutch, and 1 KE units of energy went into the reel. Review what the demon saw going from 2 S speed to 0 S if this doesn't add up for you. (Fig. 4). An obvious help in the heat loss problem is to apply only enough voltage to cause the motor to turn at 1 S. In this case, the reel will gain 1 KE units of energy, and the motor will absorb only 1 H units of heat. This is fine; 2 H units of heat are saved. But an important advantage was lost. It takes much longer to accelerate the reel when only the lower voltage is applied. Part of the penalty paid for rapid acceleration is greater heat loss.

The above discussion is not mathematically rigorous. There are certain losses in a DC motor which are stated as commutator losses, brush losses, windage losses and so forth. However, as previously stated, this is not a mathematical treatise on clutches. To a first approximation, the losses in the motor are as stated above. And the losses go up very nearly proportionally to the voltage applied during acceleration, proportionally to the no load speed.

Let us consider for a moment the heat loss in a DC motor when a reel is stopped. A DC motor has no stopped speed. That is, we can't energize a DC motor and cause it to stand still. The motor will either turn forward or backward. The reels can be stopped by plugging the motor. To plug a motor is to energize it in such a manner that it tries to reverse its direction. If the reel is turning at speed S, the motor is energized to go at speed $-2$ S. And the clutching losses are still proportional to the speed change, and the difference in speeds of the reel and the clutch.

In relation to the clutch, the reel has a speed of 3 S. (1 S— $(-2S)$) This is apparent energy of 9 KE. When the reel is stopped, the reel has an apparent energy of 4 KE in relation to the clutch. (5 H heat is lost in the clutches.)

The energy table looks like this:

### Table VI.

| Location of Energy | Beginning | End |
|---|---|---|
| Reel | 1 KE | 0 KE |
| Clutch | 0 H | 5 H |
| Energy available to motor from the line | 4 KE | 0 KE |
| Totals | 5 | 5 |

Anyone who has watched the wattmeter measuring power to a plugging motor knows that plugging is hard on the motor. And this chart shows why it is hard. Internal to the motor, the back EMF of the motor does not resist the applied voltage, but it adds to the applied voltage. Line voltage and motor voltage add during plugging instead of opposing as normally.

### ac motors

At the present time AC motors are not very popular as direct coupled energy sources on digital tape drives. (They are the most popular type on analog recorders.) Part of this is because of the power switching problem in AC motors. When motors are used to accelerate the reels directly, all the power must be switched electrically. Previously, the only device which could do this nicely was a gas filled thyratron. Because of the ground filament in the tube, a gas filled thyratron presents a problem in switching AC. Switching pulsating DC for DC motors is an easier job for thyratrons. Also, many drives were designed to use single phase AC. Therefore, a second phase would have to be developed in the drive to use AC motors as reel drives. Now that we have solid state thyratrons (SCR's) one or two tape drives have appeared on the market using AC motors as reel drives. See Figure 11 for example. Let's examine why this is so.

**Fig.11**—REAR VIEW OF A DIGITAL DRIVE USING AC REEL MOTORS. The two large horizontal AC induction motors are the standard of the industrial world because of their simplicity and reliability. *Courtesy GE Computer Department.*

Ninety-five percent of all industrial horsepower comes from AC induction motors. From an engineering viewpoint, an AC induction motor is an answer to a prayer. An induction motor has one moving part, the rotor. There are no commutators or slip rings.

And the rotor is a fused combination of iron and copper or aluminum. It can stand a very high temperature. If the power can be controlled, the AC motor is a better choice for reel drive than a DC motor. The drive clutch speed for the AC motor is always the synchronous speed of the motor, which may be plus or minus to the reels. And the rotor can better take the heat losses of starting and stopping. Unlike a DC motor, the applied voltage will not make the motor run faster or slower, it is only the synchronous speed that is significant. Clutching heat losses will be very nearly what the demon sees riding the reels and comparing against the synchronous speed of the motor.

## mechanical clutches

Mechanical clutches are those which establish a mechanical connection between the reel and a rotating member or a fixed member. The clutch may magnetically establish this connection. AC and DC motors do not establish an actual mechanical connection.

The most common type of mechanical clutch is one in which we rub one piece of material against another during clutching action. The clutch in automobiles is this type of clutch. The second type of mechanical clutch is one that causes a third type of material to be forced between two existing types of material. A powdered iron clutch is an example. When the clutch is to be engaged, a magnetic field pulls powdered iron in contact with the driving surface and the driven surface. The magnetic field plays little or no part in the transmission of energy. Its function is strictly to get the iron powder forced in between the driven and driving clutch members.

The advantage of the mechanical clutch is that it is small for the amount of power that can be transmitted. And a mechanical clutch can be run hotter than an AC or DC motor. Also, most mechanical clutches have a long life. However, it must be pointed out that when mechanical clutches are used as the driving sources for the reels, an electric motor is needed to drive the clutch. The electric motor does not have to dissipate the start and stop heat because that is done in the mechanical clutch.

## practical designs

Various manufacturers have taken different approaches to solving the clutching problems in the reels. Figure 10 pictures a DC motor reel control. The motor takes all the heat of starting and stopping. The motor is large enough to dissipate all this heat. Notice also that the motor is directly mounted to the frame so that motor heat can be conducted to the frame. Shock mounting would have reduced the motor's start-stop capacity.

In Figure 12 is an example of a manufacturer who has added a brake to the DC motor. Incidently, the drives pictured in Figure 10 had brakes also, but these were only used to keep the reels from turning

**Fig. 12**—REAR VIEWS OF DIGITAL DRIVES USING DC MOTORS AND DISK BREAKS. At left: Two large DC motors are used to drive the reels. In addition disk breaks are employed to stop the reels. This reduces the heat load on the motors. Notice the ducts directing air onto the brakes. *Courtesy Control Data Corp.*

At right: The upper and lower motors at the left are DC series reel motors. The flange mounting of the motors and the disk brakes handle the heating problems caused by starting and stopping. *Courtesy Datamec Corp.*

when motor power was off. The clutch brake pictured in Figure 12 is used to stop the reels in normal start and stop cycling.

The manufacturers reduced the amount of heat loss in the reel's motor by adding a disk brake. A DC motor is used to accelerate the reel to the desired speed. But a disk brake stops the reel turning. This presents a considerable saving in heat loss in the motor. The only way that a motor can stop a reel is to plug, or reverse, the motor. It was previously demonstrated that plugging a motor used up four additional units of heat (Table 6). The additional disk brake removes 5 H units of heat from the motor, and it saves the loss of 4 H units in the system. A motor and a disk brake make a good working pair.

## other heat saving devices—speed control

Information can also be used to reduce heating. For example, suppose that the empty reel must turn at 560 rpm to match capstan speed. It will then only have to turn at about 280 rpm to match capstan speed when the reel is full. The effective diameter of the reel changes as tape is taken off or added to a reel.

A reel system may not know how much tape is on the reels. When the reels are told to go, they will go to the highest possible speed, even if the reel is full. But as we have seen, heat loss goes up as the square of speed. Therefore, overspeeding caused additional heat loss. Information can be supplied to the reels which describe just how fast the reels must turn. The reel system will then turn only fast enough to meet the needs of the capstan. No heat is generated because of overspeeding.

The more sophisticated tape drives use a tachometer to measure the speed of the tape coming off the reel. This speed information is fed back to the reel drives. The addition of a tachometer reduces reel overspeed and saves heat. The tachometer may also give the reels a smoother running appearance.

### speed range

The desire to save some of the overspeed heating is one reason for a difference between IBM and NAB reels. The ratio between the full reel's diameter and the empty reel diameter controls the amount of overspeed in a simple reel control system. The ratio between the diameter of a full reel and an empty one is less on an IBM reel. Therefore, if a system is designed to handle only IBM reels, it has a smaller speed range to handle.

### motor compatibility

An electric motor can deliver more power by turning faster. The torque available from a motor is not so dependent on the actual speed as on the slip speed. (Slip speed is the difference between synchronous speed and actual speed.) Line frequency allows speed of 3,600 rpm for AC motors. Normal DC motors easily run at 0 to 4,000 rpm. But reels of tape are seldom required to turn faster than 600 rpm. So the direct coupling of motors to reels is not always speed compatible. One drive has recently come on the market with belt connection between the reels and the drive motor. This reduces the difference between operating speed and synchronous speed; heat losses are reduced. Since the drive motors are turning faster, the motor cooling fan works better. This also reduces the heat problem. Increasing the motor speed with a belt drive reduces heat loss for electric motors, matches motor characteristics better to reel characteristics, and improves internal cooling of the motor.

## design limits

At this point it is well to set down the design limits of a reel drive. By knowing these limits, we can design a better drive, and know what to look for when buying a drive.

The first limit on a reel drive is torque, how hard we can twist a reel of tape before it will slip. The terms *cinching spooking* and *pack slippage* are not unknown terms in the field. These terms all mean the same thing. While a reel of tape was being accelerated or decelerated, the outer layers of tape slip with relations to the inner layers. When this happens, the tape at the point of slippage is squeezed into accordian layers, or the tape is folded over. These folded-over sections cannot be read. It frequently means that the reel is ruined. One cause of this is reel drive twisting too hard on the reels. A poor tape pack will increase the possibility of pack slippage. However, any pack can be slipped if it is twisted hard enough. There is a fixed limit on how hard the reels can twist a pack. This limit can be lowered by improper tape tension, and by temperature and humidity cycling.

The next design limit is on how fast heat can be dumped into the reel drives. If reels are accelerated to operating speed and then stopped at the maximum rate possible, the reel drives may burn out or fail to function. The heating capacity of the reel drive limits how many times a minute the reels can be accelerated and stopped. Tape will be pulled out of the buffer storage when this design limit is reached. The design limit is the rate at which reels can be accelerated and stopped. This rate must not exceed the heat limits of the reel drive, or the demands of buffer storage and capstan.

A good simple test of this limit is to program a drive to cause tape to go forward until the reels just reach operating speed. Then stop the tape and reverse it until the reels come to a halt. Then start the tape going in a forward direction again. Repeat this action for an hour. If the temperature of the reel drive does not exceed design limits, and tape is never pulled out of the buffer storage, it is a reasonable assurance that the reel drive is well designed.

The final design limit on reel drives is the electrical power switching. Somehow the electric power to the drive motors, or clutches, must be switched on and off. This rate may be 100 times a second. Or it may be one or two times a second. Whatever the rate, the power switching device must handle a sizable amount of power. Mechanical switches, gas-filled thyratrons, thyratron like transistors, are being used in this job.

Reliability is a problem in these devices. Only a long-term test or an engineering judgment can give an indication on a particular design.

## in summary

The starting and stopping of tape reels involves certain heat losses. These heat losses are inherent in acceleration from fixed drive sources. The bigger the spread between drive sources speed and the reel, the greater is the heat loss. DC and AC motors alone have been used to drive start-and-stop reels. However, friction brakes have an inherent advantage over motors in stopping reels. Combination of motors and mechanical brakes are being used. Also some drives use friction clutches rather than direct couple motors to start and stop reels.

Reels design, speed sensing, and other devices are used to reduce the heat problem. The amount of torque that can be applied, the heating that can be absorbed, and the ability to switch power rapidly, are the design limits of a reel drive. A simple hour test can determine if a drive is within its design limits. Many weeks are required to determine reliability.

## CHAPTER 2. Questions

1. What is the big difference between an analog drive and a digital drive?
2. What are the three forms of energy?
3. What is the difference between energy, work, and power?
4. Consider a reel going from speed 1S to a speed of minus 1S. This is done by clutching into a shaft which is constantly turning at minus 1S. What is the heat loss in the clutch?
5. What limits the maximum amount of torque that can be applied to the reels?
6. What limits the number of times that a reel can be started and stopped in a minute?
7. Why are DC motors most commonly used as reel drives?
8. Describe a quick test to prove the adequacy of the reel design.

# 3 buffer storage

**TAPE REELS ARE SLOW.** They can be started up in a minimum of 150 to 250 MS. But the demands of the capstan are fast. A capstan can start up and be taking tape in 10 MS or less. If there were no storage between the capstan and the reels, tape would be broken. The capstan would start up and pull tape in 10 MS or less, but the reels wouldn't be able to deliver any for 150 to 250 MS. This condition calls for a slack loop of tape between the reels and the capstan drive. This is called a "buffer" storage of tape.

The buffer storage of tape is designed to make up the difference between the demands of the capstan and the capability of the reels. In the long run (250 MS) the reels have to be as fast as the capstan. But tape is broken in the short run (under 250 MS). It might be expressed that the function of the buffer storage is to keep the tape tension from getting too high or too low.

In the main, control of tape tension is the principal function of buffer storage. Like so many devices, once we have to have buffer storage many other functions can be assigned to it. For example, buffer storage is used to sense how much tape is in storage. The reels can then be started and stopped independently of the capstans. Buffer storage can do tape guiding so that tape will be fed to the head guides squarely.

Buffer storage can also be used to align the tape going onto the reels. The basic job of controlling tape tension requires the buffer storage to keep a reserve supply of tape available. The reel-to-capstan speed differences must balance out.

## tape tension

The need for proper tape tension is one of the subtle niceties of a tape drive. Most drives will operate very nicely with a tension of between four to sixteen ounces per half-inch width, at least for a while. Then, strange things happen to the reels of tape that come off that drive, and people complain that there is noise in the inter-record gaps. We will soon find that some of the reels cannot be read because of cinching or spooling. Part of the reels have a very high error rate. Let's examine how and why, and then we can better understand the function of tension in a tape drive.

## effect of tension on reels

When tape is wound on a reel with uniform tension, the tension changes after the tape is on the reels. Let us wind the reel of tape about one-third full of tape. Then we will mark the tape for one full revolution of the reel. The two ends of the mark will just come together. Now let us continue to wind tape on the reel. Succeeding layers of tape press down on the marked layer. Because the tape under the marked layer is not rigid, this tape gives under the pressure, forced by the outside wraps of tape. The marked tape goes in, it encircles a smaller diameter loop, and a shorter distance around. If the ends of the marks are to remain together the tape length must shorten. The only way tape can be shortened is to give up some of its tension. Putting any tape in tension makes it a little longer. The tension can be taken out by allowing the tape to return to its original length.

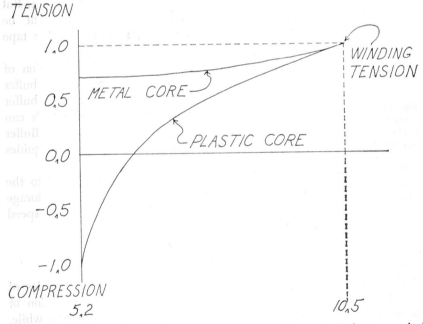

**Fig. 13—TAPE TENSION ON A REEL.** These curves describe the tension in the tape packed on a plastic or metal reel. Because a metal reel core is much stiffer, tape on a metal reel never goes into compression. Since there is no force between layers due to length change, plastic hubs are more likely to allow a cinched pack. *Courtesy Pyral Co. France.*

The same effects and results are being felt by every other piece of tape in the reel. A plot of the tape tension on a reel is shown in Figure 13. Notice that the first layer of tape on a plastic reel has tension minus T (compression). This tension changed because of a non-rigid hub. The next layer sees the flexible first layer, plus the compressed hub. Consequently the second layer may have its wrap diameter change a little less as a result of inward pressure from other layers of tape. The third layer then sees two layers of tape plus a doubly compressed hub.

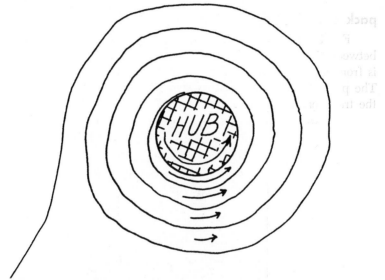

**Fig. 14—TORQUE TRANSMISSION.** This diagram shows how the torque from the hub is transmitted through successive layers of tape in order to rotate the entire pack. The transmission depends on layer to layer friction, which depends on tape tension. If tension forces are low, friction forces are low, and the pack may slip when accelerated.

This process continues. At about a third the distance from the hub to the outside of the tape, tape is neither in tension or compression. The effects in a metal core hub are much less pronounced. Tape is always in aixial compression and circumferential tension.

The downward pressure on each wrap is increased by every layer of tape above it. As wrap diameters farther and farther from the hub are considered; there are fewer layers of tape above to consider. So the downward pressure is reduced the farther we go from the hub.

The curve shown in Figure 13 will vary. If the backing material of the tape is changed the curve will change. If tape tension is changed, the curve will change. If tape tension is not uniform, the curve will change. For uniform tension of winding, the general shape of the curve will be as shown.

Now let's examine the function of tape tension in a reel of tape. Consider the acceleration of a real of tape, dumping tape off the reel (Fig. 14). Torque, or a twisting action, is applied to the hub. This torque is transmitted by the successive layers of tape so that all the layers of tape are turned. But how is this torque transmitted through the layers of tape? It is by friction. A layer tends to turn because it is in force contact with a lower layer. And so it continues. It is the friction between the layers that transmits the torque or twist.

### pack spooking or cinching

Friction between layers is a result of the materials and the pressure between the materials. The materials are oxide and backing. The oxide is from the layer above. The backing material is from the layer below. The pressure between the two layers is a result of two sources. One is the transmission of pressure from the upper layers through to the hub.

**Fig. 15**—PROGRAMMED TENSION TAPE WINDER. Besides serving as an off tape drive rewinder, the machine counteracts the problem shown in Fig. 13. The tension in the tape is varied as the tape is rewound. Maximum tension occurs about half way in the rewind. *Courtesy General Kinetics Inc.*

The pressure from the very top layers is transmitted through every layer to the hub. The second source of pressure is that which is generated by the individual tape wrap tension itself. When a tape loop was originally wrapped, it generated downward pressure independent of the layers above it.

A third of the way from the hub, the tape layer friction is lowest. This is because the pressure passed downward is not maximum, and self-generating, tape tension, pressure is zero. The total layer-to-layer pressure is lowest. And if tape is going to slip, cinch, or spook as a result of a reel acceleration, it is going to do it right here, where layer friction is lowest. This is the explanation of cinching occuring at about one-third the distance from the hub.

This is a very serious problem in a computer room. Pack slippage damages the tape so that it cannot be read. If the particular reel that has experienced pack slippage is a master reel, the computer run may have to be made over. If the master reel is very old, this may be difficult because the source documents are no longer available. If your computer room is experiencing pack slippage, get the situation corrected. This can be disastrous. Ampex Corporation recommends that tape stored more than one year be rewound.[1] Figure 15 shows an off-line rewinder put out by General Kinetics Inc.

## other causes of cinching

We have seen that loss of downward pressure or a reduction in inter-layer friction can result in pack slippage. What other factors can cause these two changes? Let's take the easier one first. The friction between the two layers can only be changed by changing the material, or the co-efficient of friction. When a lubricant is added, the co-efficient of friction goes down. The possibility of pack slippage goes up. One of the lubricants is oil or dirt off the tape drive itself. Oil or greasy dirt, spread over 10 or 12 inches of tape, is enough to cause pack slippage.

One of the tape drive manufacturers was considering adding a dry lubrication to the tape as it passed thru the drive. Fortunately, they experienced pack slippage in the lab before the change was made to the machines.

How downward pressure can change is a more difficult question. First of all, let's do some figuring. The backing material in one-half inch tape will expand about 0.03% for 10 ounce tension. The tape will expand about 0.001% for each percent increase in relative humidity. And it will expand about 0.002% for each degree Fahrenheit increase in temperature. This says that a 30% change in relative humidity, or a 15° change in temperature, will equal the expansion of 10 ounces of tension. If no other factors come into play, the winding tension would be lost with the above changes in humidity and temperature. The other facet that comes into play is that the thickness of the material also

---

1. Ampex Magnetic Tape Trends, Bulletin Number 2, July 1963.

changes with temperature and humidity. Lengthening of the tape tends to take tension out, thickening of the tape tends to put tension into the tape. A thicker tape increases tape pack diameter which puts the layer above into tension.

Generally speaking, temperature and humidity cycling which is gradual and uniform throughout the pack will not cause pack slippage. However, if the temperature or humidity changes are rapid or not distributed evenly, pack slippage can occur. There have been some cases of the pack spooking in the tape vaults. The tape was put away in good condition, and the temperature or humidity cycling in the tape vaults caused outer layers of tape to slip with respect to the inner layers.

### effects of tension on error rate, write flap

Most magnetic tape drives depend on tape-to-head contact for proper writing. The magnetic field set up by the write head becomes ineffective at 0.001 inches from the write head. Thus it becomes very important that tape-to-head contact be maintained. Some early drives used felt pressure pads to hold the tape in contact with the head; other drives used a large angle of wrap. One drive uses an air pressure pad. The tension in the tape caused by the buffer system is an important means of holding the tape in contact. When tape is wrapped over a head, the downward force of the tape on the head is a direct function of tape tension. Thus the tension in the tape caused by the buffer storage is directly responsible for good writing.

When the tape is pulled due to starting, a wave motion is sent down thru the tape. This wave motion is similar to water waves. If the wave is not damped out, the tape will leave the head. Old data will not be erased, and new data will not be recorded. High, even, tape tension helps head guides to control tape flap. (See Chapter 5, "Head Guides.")

### other functions of buffer storage

The amount of tape in the buffer is used to control the speed and direction of the reels. In some drives, the rate of change of the tape loop is used to control the reels also. Still other drives use these two factors plus the rate of tape being dumped into the buffer. The amount of information used to control the reels goes from the simple to the complicated.

### three elements of information

In Figure 16 is a simple reel buffer capstan machine. The points labeled **A**, **B**, and **C** are the measurement points. At point **A** is the place to determine how fast tape is being put into buffer storage by the reels. We cannot tell by the speed of the reels. The diameter of the reels keep changing. The reels' speed has no direct relationship to the tape speed. The tape speed must be measured after it leaves the reel at **A**.

The second point of interest is the bottom of the tape loop **B**. The exact position of **B** can be determined with different accuracy. One

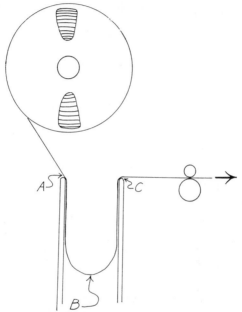

**Fig. 16**—GENERALIZED BUFFER CONTROL. There are three points where movement of the tape can be checked. At "A" the amount of tape fed into buffer storage can be measured. This is also an indication of reel speed. At "B" the total of all the tape in storage can be checked. At "C" the amount of tape taken out of storage can be checked. The amount "B" will equal the difference between "C" and "A".

can say that the location of **B** is exactly 8.1 or 8.3 inches from the top. Or we can say that the loop is between 8 and 9 inches from the top. There are drives that use both methods of determining the position of the tape loop.

The measurement that is made at point **C** is the speed out of the buffer storage. No drives determine this information from point **C**. The reason is that the information can more easily be obtained from other sources. Since the capstan has a constant speed, sensing the "go" electronics will indicate the speed at **C**. Also, since the speed at **A** is measured and the movement of **B** can be measured, the speed at **C** can be figured. The speed of the tape at **A, B,** and **C** is needed to completely control the reel speed. But the three speeds are not independent. If any two are known, the other one can be figured. The location of point **B** is always sensed. If a more sophisticated control is needed, then the speed of movement of **B,** and/or the speed of **A** is measured.

## what control is needed?

This book is not intended to go into all the calculations and design considerations necessary to determine a reel servo. However, some of the considerations will be pointed out. The amount of tape in a buffer system is dependent on reel inertia, reel clutch torque, tape velocity over the head, possibility of reel overspeed, high speed reversal of tape over the head (backspace, rewind) and sophistication of the sensing system. The most sophisticated sensing system will take into account the exact position of tape loop and the velocity of tape in and out of the buffer. The system will know reel inertia as it changes, and be able to calculate the proper steady state loop position for all combinations of the above. By the amount of the uncertainty of the above data, the size of the buffer must be increased. The list of elements that affect the buffer is enough to convince one that a sophisticated sensing system is complicated and expensive. Fortunately a good economic trade-off is possible. The trade-off is between the amount of storage and sophistication.

For example, to sense the exact position of a loop may be expensive. However, sensing elements every two inches will locate the loop within plus or minus one inch. This tolerance increases the required loop storage by only two inches.

In order to demonstrate how elements of the system affects design, let's consider a hypothetical system, with the following simplifying assumptions:

1. *A full reel of tape can be linearly accelerated until tape comes off the reels at capstan velocity (V) in 100 ms after start.*
2. *The reel can reach twice capstan velocity (2V) in 200 milliseconds. [Twice capstan velocity is needed so that tape from an empty reel can reach capstan (V).]*
3. *A record is being read which is 200 milliseconds long, and rewind takes place after this record.*
4. *The forward-to-reverse delay is small, i.e., 10 milliseconds or less.*
5. *The control system is the simplest possible. Reels are commanded to go full speed forward until the tape loop is restored to a fixed position. Then the reels are commanded to stop. Direction of reel rotation is determined by the loop being above or*

*below the fixed point. (This condition is an unstable situation, but will be used to illustrate the elements of the control.) Figure 17 shows the action.*

At zero time the tape loop and reel are at rest. Tape velocity over the head changes from zero to V. Actual capstan acceleration can be ignored because it is small (0.2-1.0 MS). At 100 MS loop excursion is —1 (½ V x 100 MS). This is the point at which the tape coming off the reel must just match the velocity of tape being fed into the capstan. The loop has been stabilized. If reel inertia were less, or higher "clutch"

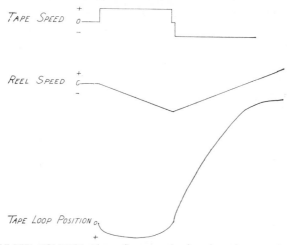

**Fig. 17**—SIMPLE REEL CONTROL. These three graphs show how the very simplest reel control would react to a rapid reversal of tape. Loop excursion is maximum because the time of tape forward was chosen to cause this.

torques could have been used, a smaller loop excursion could have resulted. Also, lower tape velocity over the head would result in smaller loop excursions. The reel continues to accelerate until the loop returns to zero location. By then (200MS) the reels are spilling tape at 2 V, and the loop has returned to zero. Just then capstan tape velocity reverses to —V. Now tape is being dumped into the storage at a velocity of 3 V, 2 V from the reels and V from the capstan. At 400 MS the reel is stopped and only the capstan is dumping tape into the storage. At 500 MS the reel has reversed direction and has accelerated to compensate for capstan tape velocity. At this point, the tape loop has stabilized after an excursion of —1 (½ V x 100 MS) + 9 (½ V x 100 MS) or 10 (½ V x 100 MS)

Now let us analyze the cause of these excursions to illustrate how each piece of sensing data can be used to reduce tape loop excursions or to reduce the required amount of buffer storage.

The excursion at 100 MS is a function of clutch torque, reel inertia, and capstan velocity. To reduce this excursion would require a change in the physical elements. No new information about loop position could reduce this excursion. However, the excursion at 500 MS can be reduced. Sensing elements could determine that the loop stabilized at 100 MS; then the reel clutch could be commanded to stop accelerating. The reel would not overspeed with adequate sensing and control. Without reel overspeed, the excursion at 500 ms would be less. The excursion would be less because, (1) less time would be needed to reverse the reel from velocity V rather than from 2 V, (2) the reversal would have started from a location of —1 (½ V x 100 MS) instead of zero.

Figure 18 is an improved version of Figure 17. The dashed line shows the loop excursion if the reels overspeed. At point **A**, the system logic recognized that the capstan reels were turning fast enough to keep up with the capstan. Hence they were not told to turn any faster. This control does not reduce the loop excursion at point **A**. The benefit from this control comes when the capstan reverses. The reel does not have to reverse from as high a speed as previously.

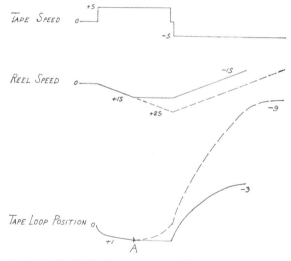

**Fig. 18—SMARTER REEL CONTROL.** These three graphs show how the loop excursions can be reduced by sensing and using the information that can be read in Fig. 16. The reels were never made to operate faster than just to meet the demands of the capstan. Thus the reels are in a better position to react to the rapid tape reversal.

Because the reel does not need to overspeed, the reel is able to stop in 100 MS instead of 200 MS. It was reversed in 200 MS versus 300 MS. And loop excursion was reduced from 9(½ V x 100 MS) to 3(½ V x 100 MS). This reduction took place because the reels were not overspeeding when the capstan reversed, and because the tape loop was as far as possible in the forward direction.

This example is as simple as possible. It shows how overspeed and position sensing can reduce loop excursions. It shows how buffer storage can be made smaller. The control does become a good deal more complicated when short records are introduced. Short records may require the loop to stabilize at a point half-way up the buffer storage. To obtain a minimum buffer storage a peculiar loop position is required for each combination of capstan starts and stops.

The particular drive that we are interested in may have a very sophisticated reel control, and smaller buffer storage. Another drive may have a less complicated reel control but a bigger buffer storage. Either system is equally good. It is strictly an economic trade-off between how smart the reel control is, and how big the buffer storage is. We don't care which system is used, as long as we get the best price.

## buffer guiding

For a overly long time the buffer guiding has been overlooked by tape drive manufacturers. Some drives do not utilize buffer guiding at all. The buffer system guides are so wide that the head guides completely control the lateral motion of the tape, but the trouble with this is that head guides have close tolerance. Therefore, a severe load of correction is placed on these guides. This means that the guides use more force on the edge of the tape than they should have to use. Head guides would work more easily if they only had to make minor corrections instead of gross compensation for tape weaving.

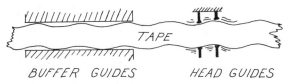

**Fig. 19—TAPE WIGGLES THROUGH THE GUIDES.** This sketch shows how tape wiggles as it passes through the head guides. Notice how buffer guides even out variations. Tape wiggle is a prime contributer to dynamic skew. Dynamic skew stands in the way of higher recording densities. The dimensions in this drawing are greatly exaggerated.

Tape weaves back and forth as it passes over the head like a drunk going down a sidewalk. These weaves can be demonstrated by unrolling a reel of tape on the floor. The tape will not come off straight; there will be a curve in the tape. Some manufacturers even specify this curvature, at greater than 100 inches. An infinite radius of a curvature is straight tape.

If the buffer storage is able to guide the tape close to the channel where it belongs, the guides at the head do not have to exert so much corrective force. It is high force on the tape which causes edge damage.

There is some indication that head guiding may not be needed or desirable (see Chapter 5). If buffer guiding is accurate enough and close enough, there is no need for guides at the head. Buffer guiding is much better because it works off over a large area of the tape (Fig. 19). Force per inch of edge is less. Also, there is an 8.5 inch cyclic weave in some tape. (The tape weave every 8.5 inches seems to be related to the circumference of the splitting wheels.) Buffer guiding is more effective in handling these variations.

There is one other place where buffer guiding is important. This is the guiding of tape into the reels. If one layer of tape sticks out of the pack as much as 0.030 inch, it is subject to serious damage. If an operator touches the edges of the poorly wound pack, there is edge damage and trouble. If he touches the edges of the good pack, there is no problem. Operators shouldn't touch the edge of either pack, but people are people.

When the tape is properly guided and tensioned onto the tape reel, the edge of the tape does not need the reel flanges. A good running tape drive will wind and unwind tape from a reel hub without any flanges. I personally have seen it done a number of times. The next question is, why do we need close tolerance reels? Answer, we don't. Since the tape edge should never touch the reels, the tape doesn't care if the reels are machined with precision or not. If the drive is not packing the tape well, and the tape does touch the reel, a smooth reel may help us to live with a bad situation.

The flanges on a reel are to protect the tape from the operator. They should have nothing to do with the guiding of the tape onto the reel. When a tape is running, all the flanges of the reel can do is damage the edge of the tape. Close tolerance reels can reduce this damage.

### air versus mechanical buffering

There are three principal ways that a store of tape can be maintained in a low inertia form. One is a loop of tape maintained with an air differential. The second is a loop or loops of tape maintained on movable fingers or buffer arms. The third is to maintain a store of tape in a tensionless basket. Machines that use very short strips of tape (6 to 8 inches) are not considered tape drives in this book.

At the present time, most tape drives being manufactured use air as part of the buffer storage. The air loop of tape may be only 10 percent of the total storage, but experience has proven that only air loops are fast enough to respond to the capstan demands (Fig. 20).

To understand why only air loops of tape are fast enough, let us jump forward and consider the capstan system. A capstan system will accelerate a tape from zero to read velocity in 0.2 to 1 MS. This is not to say start time is 0.2 to 1.0 MS, but rather actual acceleration

**Fig. 20**—AIR AND MECHANICAL TAPE BUFFERING. This is recognition that only air is fast enough to respond to capstan demands. The capstans pull tape out of air chambers. Mechanical arms supply the bulk of tape buffering. *Courtesy GE Computer Department.*

takes place in 0.2 to 1 MS. This requires a buffer frequency response of 1,000 cycles to 5,000 cycles. There is no mechanical system which had a response frequency in this range when used to store magnetic tape. Only air has the force-to-inertia ratio needed to respond to 0.2 MS acceleration time.

Those tape drives which were designed without air loops have high tension transience in the tape and develop loose tape loops. To overcome these problems, felt pads are used to damp out the tension transience and to prevent the tape from "flopping" as it passes over the read-write head. These solutions did not solve the problems, but hid the effects.

This is not to argue that buffer arms are not good; rather, it is to point out that buffer arms alone are not sufficient. A tape drive with only air pocket storage is not necessarily better than a drive with buffer arms and air pocket storage. Other considerations such as cost, size, and difficulty of design should be the predominant factors of consideration.

## design factors

In the design of a system, there are three principal factors to consider. First, what sensing means will be employed? Direct tape sensing could be a tachometer geared to the tape. Indirect sensing could be pressure changed as the loop goes by a port. Second, how much storage is needed will depend on tape velocity, reel inertia, reel clutch, and limitation on program commands. Third, what physical volume is available for mounting the drive? Does the volume permit long air chambers, or must buffer arms or tape bins be used? These factors are explored fully when tape drives are designed.

One point about sensing devices should be paramount. The tape loop will move each time a record is read or written. In addition, overshot and hunting can cause many more tape loop movements. Therefore any tape loop sensing device should be able to stand five hundred million loop movements before failure. Or the sensing element should be cheap and easily replaced. The sensing system must be reliable. The number of types of sensing devices which determine movement of tape loops is large. Potentiometers and synchros are used on mechanical buffer arms to measure arm and loop position. Air switches, pressure transducers, and photo cells are used in air chambers and loose bins to sense amount of tape. Tachometers are used to measure tape velocity between the reel and the buffer. Electrical signals sensing the actuator position are used to sense tape velocity between head and buffer storage. All of these devices are designed to determine what the loops are doing in the buffer storage. The signal from these devices cause the proper corrective action to be initiated in the reel "clutches."

Which of the above sensing elements should be used? How accurate should the sensing element be? These are questions which can only be answered through a consideration of the total system. The sensing devices are the inputs into the buffer control logic. When this input data is combined with knowledge of reel clutches, tape inertia, and velocity, the amount of tape buffer storage can be determined. When the amount of buffer storage is known, the type of storage can be selected.

The amount of tape storage that is needed and the tape sensors available heavily influence the type of storage selected. Also the amount of room allowed for packaging the tape drive influences the type of storage selected. There is no clear-cut answer. Technological changes change the answer too.

## what the user should look for

Any digital tape drive will have a buffer storage between the capstan and the tape reels. The user should make sure that there is an air loop next to the capstan. If there isn't such an air loop, then the user should restrict himself to sandwich tape. (Sandwich tape has plastic on both sides of the oxide.) The high tension transients are too much for a non-sandwich tape.

Next the user should determine that the buffer system is large enough to handle their job. If this is done by calculation, it can be a big job. However a simple performance test is sufficient to tell us if the tape drive will do the job. A good test is the same one described for a heat test in Chapter 2. Cause tape to go forward until the reels have just reached their top speed (usually about 200 MS). Then stop and reverse the tape until the reels have just reached their top speed in reverse. Then stop the tape and go forward again. If the forward and reverse times are adjusted so the tape goes backward a little less than it goes forward, the test will creep down the whole reel of tape. This is good, because we want to know how the drives work with an empty reel as well as a full reel. During the initial test, the tape should never become slack or taut. If the tape drive cannot pass this test, there is a good chance that it will break or cinch the tape someday.

Next we will have to make some measurements. Determine that all guides that are designed to control the tape from the edge are wider than the widest tape tolerance (½ inch tape is 0.496 to 0.500). Any edge guide that is more than 0.005 oversize should be explained. If a guide cannot control the tape to closer than 0.005, there is a question as to why it is there at all. There may be some spring guides in the tape path. These are guides that move under control of a spring. Usually these guides are near the head assembly. Be sure that these are ceramic guides. The tape oxide will cut spring loaded steel guides.

**tape tension**

One final measurement—determine what the tension of the tape is when the drive is running. Tension should be four to five ounces per quarter-inch width. This will cause the tape to be wound on reels with little danger of cinching or spooking. Now there are drives which are able to operate successfully with less than this tension. Generally these drives have packer arms that ride on the tape as it enters the reel. If a drive has low tension, and you are planning to interchange tapes, BE CAREFUL! It may be true that our drives will work fine with low tension. But when we ship reels, wound with low tension, to another site, the other site may cinch the reels. IBM compatible means record formate and tape condition.

**in summary**

The tape buffer system is used to keep the tension in the tape to a proper level. It does this by keeping a supply of tape available in loops. These loops are in air chambers, on buffer arms, or in loose bins. Many systems can be designed to sense the loops and control the reels in a satisfactory manner. As long as the system is reliable, we shouldn't care which are used. This is the manufacturer's cost problem. Only results and performance concern us. A secondary function of the buffer system is to edge-guide the tape. This guiding controls the tape into the reels and to the head.

## CHAPTER 3. Questions

1. What are the benefits of proper tape tension?
2. How can oil or dirt increase the possibility of pack slippage?
3. What are the effects of tape flap at the read and write heads?
4. Where are the three points in a tape buffer system which can be used to determine the proper command for the reels?
5. How do reel flanges aid in tape guiding?
6. Why is air storage necessary in any tape buffer system?
7. How can a tape buffer system be tested?

# 4 capstans

**BACK IN THE DAYS OF THE SAILING SHIPS,** a sailor would loop a rope around a power driven capstan to pull the ship to the dock. He might not recognize the similarity between his action and the capstan on a modern tape drive, but the similarity is there.

A tape drive depends on friction between the tape and the capstan to pull the magnetic tape across the read-write head. On most drives, the friction between the tape and the capstan is varied to cause the tape to move or not to move. In some of the more recent tape drives, the tape is held in constant contact with the capstan. The capstan is then started and stopped to pull tape across the head.

It might seem that such a small portion of the drive as the capstan does not merit a full chapter in this book. Don't be misled. After the read-write head establishes the upper writing density, the capstan establishes most of the important performance characteristics. It is the capstan system which controls:

1. *The speed of the tape over the head,*
2. *The amount of speed variation (and hence all data recording density),*
3. *The size of the inter-record gap,*
4. *Whether our program will run full-speed, or be held up with a stop delay,*
5. *How much wear the tape sees during starting.*

From this list, we can see that the capstan is an important part of the tape drive. It has one other aspect. When visitors come to the computer room, it is the reel drive which supplies all the things to see. But it generally is the capstan which supplies the audio.

## how does the pinch roller system work?

The operation of the pinch roller capstan is the ultimate in visual simplicity. An idler roller is pushed against the tape, which is pushed against the capstan. Both the idler and the tape are forced by friction to move at the speed of the capstan. And from this point on there is

**45**

nothing simple about the capstan system. Every bit of additional information must be obtained by careful analysis.

The ideal capstan system would start and accelerate the tape to running speed without any overshot, and as fast as possible. The limiting factor is how much pull the tape itself can stand without breaking. The ideal capstan would have no overshot, and no speed variation after the tape is up to speed. Also, unbalanced tension in the tape could not effect the speed. Finally, the tape could come down to zero speed without creeping. Creep is very slow movement of the tape (under 0.1 inch per second). These limits wouldn't scare most mechanical designers. They wouldn't scare him until we told him that the entire cycle (tape start, tape running and tape stop) had to be repeated a hundred times a second. A capstan system must be able to start, drive, and stop tape 100 times a second, 6,000 times a minute, 360,000 times an hour, 2,900,000 times in an eight-hour day. This tremendous speed is what makes all the other characteristics so difficult. The operation is so fast that it is even a problem to measure the characteristics.

**Fig. 21**—PINCH ROLLER ACTUATORS. Upper illustration shows the electrical to mechanical transducer with an attached roller. Notice the metal plunger opposite the black rubber pinch roller. This device requires power all during the time of engagement and is spring returned. Lower illustration shows a second type of electrical mechanical transducer which twists back and forth about 10°. The pinch roller assembly is fixed to the shaft and moves about 0.010 inches. This device requires power during the on or off thrust only. It is held in either position with permanent magnets. *Courtesy GE Computer Department.*

## what happens on start?

In any capstan system we have to have an actuator. This is a device which takes an electrical signal and produces a mechanical movement. An electric motor is such a device; so is the bell ringer on the telephone. The actuator on the tape drive is similar but much faster. The actuator on a pinch roller drive accepts a signal and moves the idler into contact with the tape and capstan.

There are a number of different styles of actuators (see Fig. 21). But each one of these is too practical, so let's design one of our own to see what the problems are. In Figure 22 is a pinch roller drive actuator.

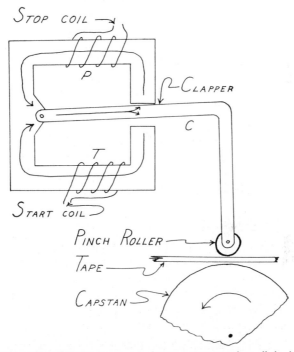

**Fig. 22—SINGLE ACTUATOR.** This is a home design actuator. It has all the basic elements. A start coil and flux path engage the pinch rollers. A stop coil and flux path pull the pinch roller from the capstan. Niceties like anti-bounce bumpers are not included in this design.

When we energize the start coil, a magnetic flux is set up around path **T**. The Clapper **C** is pulled towards the **T** coil side. When this happens, the pinch roller pushes the tape into contact with the capstan. Now the trouble begins.

The clapper and pinch roller have to move very rapidly. When the pinch roller strikes the capstan it tends to bounce. Any bounce will remove the friction between the tape and the capstan. One way to keep the pinch roller from bouncing is to have the clapper touch the pole piece on **T** side just before the pinch roller hits. This would close the magnetic circuit **T** and increase the holding force. But the pole surface must be well located. If the clapper touches the **T** pole piece too soon, the pinch roller will never touch the capstan. The pinch roller may only move a total of 0.010 inch.

We might introduce a rubber bumper to absorb the clapper energy just before the pinch roller closes. Since rubber is soft, its location tolerance can be absorbed, more or less, in a squeeze. The question is, how many days will the rubber bumper last at two million squeezes a day? This problem of pinch roller bouncing has plagued the tape drive manufacturers for some time. It is the same basic problem that we described in Chapter 2 on reel drives. How can we put energy into a system and take it out rapidly? One manufacturer used a friction slide to take the energy out of the pinch roller. But dry friction is very difficult to control. So the slide was oiled, and the oil got on the tape and collected dirt. Most manufacturers use a rubber or plastic part to absorb the energy from the clapper and pinch roller. This absorption can be subtle. For example, a plastic or rubber pinch roller can be the energy absorbing part. Sometimes leaf springs, similar to those on the back wheels of a car, are used to absorb energy. However it is done, the energy that moves the capstan pinch roller must be removed or the pinch roller will bounce and let the tape slip.

## what happens on stop?

After the tape has run awhile, 10MS or so, the stop coil will be energized. This will cause magnetic flux around loop **P**, which will pull the pinch roller from the capstan. The roller and capstan have the same bouncing problems as before. Now the clapper will bounce off the pole piece on the **P** side. It might seem that if the clapper bounces in the off position no harm is done. However, the bounce may well be enough to cause the pinch roller to contact the capstan again. A second energy absorbing part is needed to take the energy out of the clapper and pinch roller.

## how do the results look?

When engineers want to see this sort of action, they usually measure it indirectly. A common way is to record an entire length of tape with all one bits. Then the tape drive is made to start and stop under command of an oscillator. By reading the tape, we can tell just what is happening. Figure 23 is the picture we would see from a perfect drive.

Point **A** is the time when the drive was told to start. At **B**, the pinch roller just contacted the tape. By **C**, the tape is up to speed and running smoothly. A record can now be read or written. The reading or writing of data would be complete at **D**. By **E** the tape has come to a stop. Total elapsed time is .01 second, 10MS.

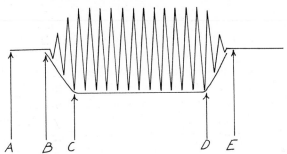

**Fig. 23—IDEAL START/STOP ENVELOPE.** This is the picture that an ideal tape drive would give an engineer during a start/stop operation. The start signal at "A" results in motion at "B". The speed of the motion increases until "C", when the speed becomes continuous until "D". The speed is reduced to zero at "E", and there are no false starts or stops.

Now let's see what really happened. The letters in Figure 24 correspond to the perfectly running drive in Figure 23. The numbered letters are the things that shouldn't happen. Tape starts at **A**; the actuator is told to move tape. At **B** the pinch roller contacts the tape. Acceleration is normal until **B1**, when the tape slows down to a stop. The pinch roller comes back in contact with the capstan at **B2**, and

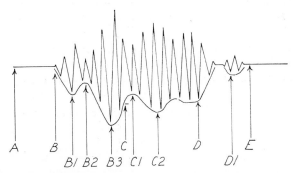

**Fig. 24—PRACTICAL START/STOP ENVELOPE.** This is a more practical example of what an engineer would see looking at the signal from a pinch roller drive during a start/stop operation. The letters correspond to those in Fig. 23. The numbered letters are variations from the ideal case. Notice how the speed variation after "C" gradually reduces in amplitude.

tape acceleration starts all over. At **B3** the tape has overshot the capstan velocity. This is due to capstan changing speed or because of elastic rebound in the tape. At point **C** the tape has come to working speed.

We will assume that the read or write operation will start here. However, the tape speed will continue to vary about the nominal for some time, perhaps .005 second, 5 MS. At **D** the read or write operation is over, and the pinch roller is disengaged.

Deceleration is normal until **D1**. The clapper and pinch roller bounce off the stop point and re-engage the tape. At point **E** the tape finally stops moving. The pinch roller may be still bouncing, but it is not hard enough to reach the tape. Elapsed time is more than before. The amount of tape used to record is also more than before. Time and tape distance are used to accommodate the false starts and stops.

The problem to the tape drive designer is to design the actuator so that false starts and stops do not occur. To do this requires putting energy into the pinch rollers and taking the energy out. There are many designs which put energy into the pinch rollers. Unfortunately, the removal of the energy is usually an afterthought. It generally is a "fix," or put in after the first model is almost running.

## other considerations

There are a good many other similar problems in the capstan area. This bounce problem was dealt with in detail so that we might have an understanding of the implication of small things. There are many other similar problems, but these will not be dealt with in such detail. Let's list some of the design problems, and the consequences of poor design.

| Capstan drive problems | Possible adverse effects |
|---|---|
| 1. Bouncing pinch rollers | 1. Longer inter-record gaps. Data recorded too densely. |
| 2. Non-square pinch rollers | 2. Tape skewed. Tape can be cut and damaged. |
| 3. Slow responding pinch rollers | 3. Holds up CPU, and can cause recording at too high a density. |
| 4. Poor reliability | 4. Can result in non-standard gaps, recording errors and excess maintenance. |
| 5. Poor cooling design | 5. Actuator will get hot at high cycle rate. Program is generally restricted to stay stopped for "X" MS after a stop. |

It should not be inferred from this chart that pinch rollers are a bad way to start and stop tape. Much is being made of air capstans that get away from all the pinch roller problems. But they find a few problems of their own.

## air capstans

In Figure 25 are examples of air capstan designs. The heart of an air capstan is a small valve **A** which is used to send air pressure or vacuum to the tape. If a vacuum is sent to the tape, the tape is pulled into contact with the capstan and accelerated. If air pressure is sent to the tape, the tape is blown away, and stopped by a brake. This appears to be easier handling of the tape. An actuator is still needed at **C**. This device is needed to move the valve back and forth. Let's make a list of some of the problems:

| Capstan drive problems | Possible adverse effects |
|---|---|
| 1. Bouncing air valve. | 1. The valve can transfer, and bounce back, slowing the start of stop. Long inter-record gaps are possible. |
| 2. Valves not seating squarely. | 2. Air leak so that the tape is started or stopped slowly. |
| 3. Slow responding actuator or capstan. | 3. This can be accommodated in the design start, and even overcome by more pressure and driving the actuator harder. Otherwise the CPU is held up, or inter-record gaps are long. |
| 4. Poor reliability (dirt or even water, in the air path, actuator adjustments). | 4. Results in non-standard gaps, recording errors, and excess maintenance. |
| 5. Poor cooling in actuator. | 5. Actuator will get too hot, limiting CPU program. |

The lists for air capstans and pinch rollers show a similarity. Each system has its problems. The location of the problem has been changed into another place. Either system can be made to work well.

## capstan drive motor

In many systems it is the capstan motor which drives the tape. This means that the motor has a speed which is controlled by the power line only. Loading and/or unloading the motor has little or no effect on the motor. The capstan motor may drive the tape directly, or through a system of belts. The diameter of the capstan and the speed of the motor control tape speed.

Industrial standards say that the tape speed must be held to plus or minus five percent. When we think of the accuracy of the synchronous motors driving our clocks, this doesn't sound tough to do. But there is a difference. The accuracy of clocks is averaged out over a day or so. If the clock falls behind twenty seconds in a day (a realistic figure), it will catch up in the evening. But tape speed is judged over a short time period, like 50 usec. Every time a character is recorded on tape, the speed must be within five percent or the data may not be readable. Basically this is a design problem. The design must be sure that the tolerance on the capstan and motor holds the tape speed to one percent

**Fig. 25—AIR CAPSTANS.** At upper left is a home design of an air capstan system. Atmospheric air and the natural pumping action of the capstan hold tape away from the capstan. When valve "A" transfers, a vacuum source pulls air from the capstan and sucks the tape in contact with the capstan. The other pictures show valves used in production tape drives. *Lower picture courtesy Midwestern Instrument Inc. Upper right picture courtesy Control Data Corp.*

or less. The start transient will eat up the other four percent of tolerance. And he must be assured that the synchronous motor that he has selected will not hunt fast enough to put him out of the speed range. (See Figure 26 for example.)

This last point should be explained. A synchronous motor has a controlled speed when averaged out over many revolutions. When a synchronous motor is first loaded, it slows down for up to a quarter revolution. A quarter revolution may be 4 MS or the time to record 400 characters at 100 KC. So synchronous speed takes on a new meaning in digital tape drives.

## power line frequency

What is the power line frequency, and how stable is it? If our installation is in a large city, or is supplied from a utility which has a large city, we will have no problem. But if, on the other hand, our company generates its own electricity, and is not tied into a larger system, our frequency may not be stable. It is a good point to check.

## nonsynchronous capstan motors

There is another means of maintaining capstan speed. This is a DC capstan motor that has a feedback. A DC motor does not have a constant speed. But with a tachometer feedback, the DC voltage can be

**Fig. 26—CAPSTAN MOTORS AND TAPE PATH.** Upper illustration shows a drive that uses two synchronous capstan motors. Note the flywheel on the rear of the motor. This is used to control high frequency speed variations. *Courtesy Control Data Corp.* Lower illustration shows a tape as it leaves air pockets and enters between pinch roller and capstan. Because regularly used magnetic tape did not show clearly, white masking tape was substituted in this picture. *Courtesy GE Computer Department,*

adjusted to make the speed a constant. This low inertia motor is used to start and stop the tape. So the motor is doing double duty. It is acting as a pinch roller clutch, to start and stop tape, and it is maintaining a constant speed. The heating problems in this motor seem to have limited themselves to the lower speed drives (under 75 inches per second). However, we can expect that better cooling and higher temperature components will allow higher speeds (Fig. 27).

## stepping motors

There is one other type of capstan drive that appears most exciting. This is an incremental or stepping drive. The capstan is able to move and stop for one character on tape. This is exciting; up to now magnetic digital tape drives have been limited to the larger computers. Tape drive systems were too expensive to tie into a weighing scale, a

**Fig. 27—NON SYNCHRONOUS DRIVE.** This rear view of a non-synchronous capstan drive shows the low inertia capstan motor (see arrow) and a small DC tachometer used to check capstan speed. *Courtesy Ampex Corp.*

cash register, or a traffic counter. But the stepping motor tape drive eliminates many problems. Such a drive doesn't need a character buffer so that its records can be written in a burst. The drive can work with the speed of the device. This type of tape drive makes it possible for the supermarket cashier to record all the transactions on a reel of magnetic tape. All the tape transactions can then be sent by tape and wire transmission to the computer center. While still on the phone, the computer will report back the number of nickels, dimes, quarters, and dollars that should be in the till.

This type of drive can give the digital computer the truly broad market and usage base that it has been lacking (Fig. 28).

## effects of capstan system on data

So far we have been dealing with the mechanics of the capstan drive system. This is background information so that the effects on recorded information can be understood.

The information from the computer is recorded on tape in precise time intervals. If the tape is not moving at a constant speed, data will

**Fig. 28—INCREMENTAL DRIVE.** Front and rear views of an incremental tape recorder. The capstan shown in the front view is very small in order to reduce the inertia reflected into the stepping motor during starting and stopping. The capstan must be able to start and stop for every character written. This drive is specified at 556 bpi and 300 steps per second. *Courtesy Precision Instrument Co.*

not be laid down on tape uniformly. The tape control has no way of knowing at what speed the tape is moving, so it must assume a uniform speed. If the speed of this tape changes, or the data is laid down in a non-uniform pattern, the controller is surprised. And a too surprised controller shows it with parity errors. The circuits in a tape controller generally allows ten percent variation from standard. However, anything more than this will cause some errors.

### cumulative speed errors

Let's see how data rates can vary by more than ten percent. During the start transient, tape speed varied about the nominal. Refer back to Figure 24. Suppose that writing takes place at a point like C1 which is a minus speed variation of six percent. When the data is read back, suppose that peak C2 coincides with the data written with the valley at C1. A valley of speed variation on writing can coincide with a peak speed variation on reading just due to changes in stopping location. If C2 is five percent high, we have an additive data transfer rate which is 11 percent above normal. We read five percent faster over data which was six percent too dense. At some densities and with some controllers this results in errors.

Service personnel and manufacturers will get around this problem by writing a bigger inter-record gap. Notice in Figure 24 that the speed variation becomes less, the longer the tape is moving. Therefore, the above problem of speed variation can be avoided. Just wait longer before writing data. Reading will be longer because the data is farther out on the tape. Both the manufacturer and the maintenance personnel would like to see the data recorded farther out on the tape. For the user this means bigger inter-record gaps. Larger inter-record gaps means a lower effective transfer rate, a slower program. Chapter 8 will deal with how to measure this, and what it means to your site.

### tape damage from pinch rollers

If a capstan system is reliable, and it doesn't generate too big inter-record gaps, the user has little concern for the capstan system. There is one point about pinch rollers that should be discussed. The implication is that because the pinch rollers accelerate tape so rapidly, pinch rollers damage tape. I don't think anyone can readily or reasonably doubt that pinch rollers can damage tape. Any part of the tape drive can damage tape. Skims in the head or sharp corners in a vacuum column can shear tape edges. The question is, *do* pinch rollers damage tape?

A pinch roller accelerates tape by squeezing the tape between a roller and the capstan. As the pressure between the roller and the tape increases, the friction increases, and tape follows the capstan. This action is very rapid, about 200 usec. (Start time is 2 to 3 MS, but actual acceleration is much shorter) It has been felt in some quarters that this very rapid action does physical harm to the tape. The writer has had no indication of this. In fact I have conducted and seen results of tests that prove rapid acceleration does not damage tape.

*This was the test:*

1. A hundred feet of tape was marked off and recorded with solid data.
2. The tape was read forward and checked for errors.
3. The tape was read backward in a start-stop mode.
4. Steps 2 and 3 were repeated until permanent errors developed.

Twenty to thirty thousand (10 to 15 thousand cycles of 2 and 3) passes of tape were necessary to wear out the tape. Some tape lasted much longer (60,000 to 80,000 cycles). When permanent errors developed they could not be associated with the pinch roller points of acceleration. The pinch rollers accelerated the tape close to the same spot each time.

After these tests were made, the writer met another group who had tested the tape for wear. This was a different drive, another manufacturer. Their test had deliberately caused the pinch rollers to accelerate in an exactly the same spot each time. Their results were very similar to mine.

Because of the pinch roller acceleration at the same spot, the tape was shiny at that point. But the data was good.

Does this mean then that pinch rollers are the ultimate capstan system? No, it does not! Air capstans, and start and stop capstans have a bright future and a number of advantages. However, the advantages to air capstans is not in reduced tape wear.

## air capstans

Air capstans also accelerate tape with friction. However, the friction between the tape and the capstan builds up gradually; this leads to a very smooth start, with little overshot.

Because of this small overshot, writing can begin as soon as tape is up to speed. At first this would make one believe that air capstans could generate smaller gaps. But this is not so. It turns out that air capstans accelerate tape so gradually that they use up a lot of distance getting up to speed. Consequently, air capstans generate inter-record gaps about the same size as pinch roller capstans do.

Start-stop capstans are those designs that keep the tape in contact with the capstan at all times. The capstan is started and stopped for each record. There are no synchronous motors that can do this. At present there are two ways to do it. Figure 27 shows an Ampex drive that uses a DC low inertia motor to start and stop the capstan for each record. This DC motor has a fiberglass disk which has wires printed on the fiberglass. Since both the motor and the capstan have very low inertia, acceleration is very fast. After the tape is up to speed, a small tachometer measures the speed of the capstan. The signal from the tachometer is compared against an internal standard to maintain "synchronous" speed.

IBM uses pinch rollers for their Hyper tape. However, they put the pinch rollers in the back of the machine. The capstan starts and stops with the tape. The starting and stopping of the capstan is with three pinch rollers in the back. One pinch roller drives the capstan and tape forward, one backward, and one is for stop. One of the big reasons for using a start and stop capstan is that it makes the automatic loading and unloading of tape much easier.

### in summary

The capstan system is designed to start and stop tape moving. There are a number of ways that this can be done:

(1) pinching the tape between a capstan and a roller,
(2) blowing the tape against a constant rotating capstan,
(3) starting and stopping the capstan itself, with tape in constant contact.

Any of the three systems will work well for us. We must not buy a drive on the basis of the method alone. Look for serviceability, good margin on the adjustments, conservative design and short consistent inter-record gaps. The best design in a capstan system is one that is so trouble-free, we forget just how it does work.

### CHAPTER 4. Questions

1. What single factor makes the capstan drive system an engineering challenge?
2. What effects does speed variation have on recorded data?
3. Why are synchronous motors used as capstan drive motors?
4. Describe three types of capstan drives.
5. Why do air capstans generate inter-record gaps about the same size as those generated by pinch roller capstans?

# 5 head guides

STRICTLY SPEAKING, all elements of the tape drive are head guides. The entire purpose of the machine is to guide a piece of tape over the head so that reading and writing can be accomplished. But in a more restricted sense, head guiding refers to those fixtures which are near to the read-write head. These fixtures constrain the tape in a lateral plane (across the width of the tape), and in a normal plane (up and down through the tape). Head guides are designed to hold the tape from wiggling over the head as reading and writing take place. See Figure 29 for tape layout.

## edge guiding

The width of tape varies as we proceed down the length of the tape. This variation is caused by the manufacturing process, as the tape

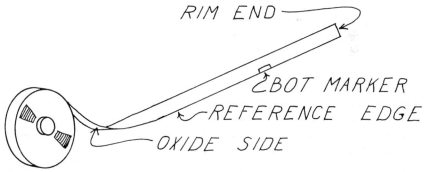

**Fig. 29—TAPE TERMINOLOGY.** This drawing shows how the reference edge of a tape can be located. With the rim end at the right, the oxide side down, the reference edge is toward the user. Another, simpler check rests in the fact that the reference edge of a tape is on the reel away from the file protect ring.

is slit from the wider rolls of tape. Most manufacturers have a slitting tolerance of 0.004 inches. Not only that, but frequently this tolerance has a pattern. Many times the tape width will repeat the pattern every 8.5 inches of tape length. This pattern is caused by a variation in the slitting wheels. Many splitting wheels are 2¾ inches in diameter.

Therefore, any variation in the wheels shows up as a pattern every 8½ inches, or once around the wheels. Tape manufacturers are reluctant to talk about their manufacturing processes. Therefore, I assume that there are some manufacturers who have different dimensions on their slitting process.

The tape drive must accommodate the above tolerance. The way the drives do it is to force the tape against a reference edge. This means that a guide on one side of the tape is spring loaded, and it forces the tape to ride against a fixed guide on the other side (Fig. 30). Which

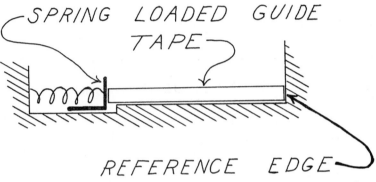

**Fig. 30—SPRING LOADED GUIDES.** Because tape varies in width, one width guide cannot accommodate all widths of tape. Hence, spring loaded guides are often used to adjust the edge of the guides to the tape.

edge is the reference edge? It really is not too important which edge is the reference edge, either edge will do. IBM originally chose the outside edge of the tape. With the oxide down, and the beginning of tape to the right, the reference edge is toward us. ASA X3.2 has now specified the same edge as the reference edge for tape interchangeability. It is a good assumption that most drives will reference this edge, the front edge.

Spring-loaded guides will keep the tape against a reference edge. In Chapter 1, a reference was made to head guide problems. Steel guides were used to guide the tape, but the new hard binder tape cut the steel guides. So this determines that any guides that are guiding the edge of tape had better be very hard material. Aluminum oxide is a common material. The edge-guiding material must be hard enough to withstand the constant abrasion of many miles of tape edge.

Guides tend to cause the tape to wiggle as it passes over the head (Fig. 31). This wiggle is a contributing factor to dynamic skew. Since no uniformity in slitting tolerance is practical, the next best that can be done is to use guides which are as far apart as possible. This will reduce the wiggle and dynamic skew to a minimum.

Edge guides must be solidly placed on either side of the head. The guides must be of some material which is harder than steel. It is possible there are no guides at all evident. The tolerance on the air chamber may be used for tape guiding. The sides of a buffer storage may be used to tack the tape as it passes over the head. The guiding surface should be spaced about four inches away from the head.

## tape flap head to tape contact

The tape must be guided over the head in another dimension. That is in the normal dimension to the tape. This is to insure that the tape doesn't lose contact with the head as it moves. Both the read and

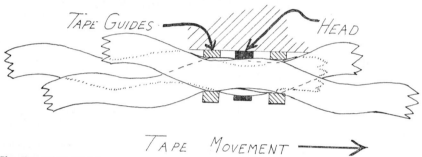

**Fig. 31—TAPE WIGGLE THROUGH THE HEAD GUIDES.** These three tape overlays show how tape can wiggle as it passes through the head guides. This variation is a prime contributor to dynamic skew, which stands in the way of higher recording densities. The dimensions are greatly exaggerated.

the write signal are very dependent on head-to-tape contact, or spacing. Most tape drives are designed to read and write with contact recording between the head and the tape. However, there have been a number of developments in the industry to indicate that these may not always be so. One tape manufacturer has developed a very thin plastic coating to separate the oxide from contact with the head. Some experience with tape drives indicates that there is the possibility that a thin air film may be maintained over the head. Both or either of these developments would, of course, have important significance. Head-to-tape contact is and has been a problem.

When the tape contacts the head, the strongest signal is recorded and read. However, tape-to-head contact causes wear to the tape and to the head. Tape wear generates oxide particles, which have enough binder in them to form a cluster. Once a cluster of oxide is formed it seems to get homesick, and the cluster returns to the tape oxide from whence it came. This oxide particle then generates an error on tape.

Any system which could separate the head and the tape oxide by a

**Fig. 32—HEAD WRAP.** The sketch shows how the tape is wrapped over the head. Tension in the tape generates a force which holds the tape in contact with the head. Most drives utilize a positive angle of wrap, but there are some that use pressure pads to maintain head to tape contact. In the photograph, the tape is wrapped over the read/write head of a digital drive. *Courtesy GE Computer Department.*

reliable 10 to 25 microinches would eliminate the head wear and the tape wear at the head.

Part of the head guide's job is to insure that there is constant tape-to-head spacing. The most common way to do this is to wrap the tape over the head (Fig. 32). This tape wrap in effect converts some of the tape tension into a normal force. This normal force holds the tape in contact with the head. A total wrap of 5 to 20 degrees is usual.

There are some drives that do not use a wrap angle to hold the tape in contact with the read-write head. These drives use a pressure pad to hold the tape in contact. The pressure pad may be air or felt. One big advantage to this type of guiding is that the tape can be pulled away from the head. When the drive goes into a rewind mode, it is desirable to insure that the tape is not wearing out during rewinding. An air pressure pad can be turned off during rewind, so that there is no head-to-tape contact during rewind.

Other drives get around the wear problem during rewind in various ways. One way is to remove the guides that cause tape wrap; IBM does this. Other drives remove pressure pads. There is a saving factor in high-speed rewind which tends to reduce wear automatically, and that is air films.

The people designing one drive were worried that they were getting excessive wear during high-speed rewind. Someone happily noticed that the read signal during rewind was not as great as it should be. The read signal is proportional to the speed of the tape. All other things being equal, if the tape rewinds four times as fast as normal, the signal should be four times as great. After checking into the reason for the low signal, they found that the higher speed of rewind was developing an air film 400 micro-inches thick—0.0004 inches. This meant that the high-speed rewind was not causing any head wear at all. It only rarely occurs in a design that things work out for you instead of against you. This was one of those happy times.

## tape flap

As we have shown in the previous paragraph, tape movement causes tape to leave the head. In the above case this was a fine thing. But when tape leaves the head during normal reading and writing, trouble is sure to follow. If tape leaves the head during writing, the previous information may not be erased, and the new information may not be recorded. If tape leaves the head during reading, the signal may be missed and parity errors will result.

What can cause tape to leave the head? Many things can cause these effects. We have already described how clusters of oxide and binder can become imbedded in the tape. When this happens, the tape is separated from the head while the cluster passes through.

A more subtle cause of head-to-tape separation is tape flap. Anyone who has watched westerns on TV has seen the snap from a bull whip. This is caused by the villain's arm putting a varying wave motion into the bull whip. The wave motion travels down the length of the whip and causes the end to flap.

In a tape drive, a pinch roller, reel transient, or some other non-linear device causes a motion in the tape. This motion propagates down the tape at the approximate speed of sound. Somehow this energy is converted into a wave motion, and the wave will pass over the head to cause head-to-tape separation or tape flap. And tape flap means trouble.

The source of the problem cannot be eliminated. A tape drive must be started rapidly. Reels must be started and stopped. And there may be other reasons for nonlinearities in tape motion. So the problem is to damp out the energy when it is put into the tape. Generally this is not difficult, if the problem is recognized. All that is necessary is to restrict the tape so that a wave cannot pass. A simple noncontacting guide that rubs against the tape only when a tape flap occurs is sufficient to prevent tape flap (see Fig. 33). Of course a felt pressure pad will

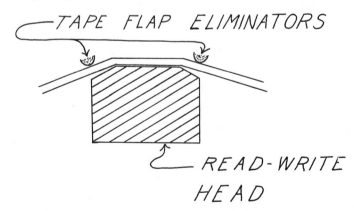

**Fig. 33—FLAP ELIMINATOR.** When tape is started very rapidly, wave movement is put into the tape. This wave may cause the tape to leave the head. Bumpers or edge-less guides, located as shown, have been used to knock out any tape flap.

eliminate flapping of the tape. Many times the normal guiding thru the machine will eliminate tape flap. If this is not the case, provisions must be made to eliminate the flap or trouble is sure to follow.

## erase heads

This subject does not strictly belong under a chapter on guiding. However, it doesn't seem to belong anywhere else. So let's spend a little time discussing the problem and advantages.

The erase head prevents any previous history from affecting the bit pattern on tape. Let's take a good look at how these benefits occur.

Assume that the tolerance on the one drive caused it to record a track, as **A** in Figure 34. The second drive, which didn't have an erase head, recorded a track like **B**. There is a small track **C**, which is not

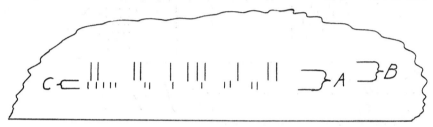

**Fig. 34—NOISE DUE TO GUIDING VARIATION.** This is an example of how noise can be left on a tape due to the variation in tape guiding. Track "A" was written first. Then track "B" did not line up perfectly. An erase head passing over this area would eliminate the problem. If an erase head had passed over this area before "B" was written, the sliver would not exist.

completely taken out by B's writing. If drive **A** tries to read this tape this small track **C** may be picked up by the read head, and cause errors. So an erase head relieves the problem of head guiding. An erase head prevents any sliver tracks from developing.

## noise in the gap

*Noise in the gap* is a miscellaneous collection of bits which are left in the inter-record gap. If the drives were very consistent in their guiding, starting, and stopping, we would not have heard the words *Noise in the gap.* However, start-stop times are not perfect, various manufacturers have different combinations of start-stop times. And guiding tolerance does vary. It is in the inter-record gap that write heads are

**Fig. 35—NOISE IN THE GAP.** This figure demonstrates noise in the inter-record gap. Many times the bits written in the gap are not as strong as the data bits.

turned on or off. Most write and erase heads leave noise on the tape when they are turned off. This is not inherent, but it is the way the write circuits happen to be designed. Therefore, when write and erase heads leave noise in the inter-record gap, we have situations very similar to the one described for Figure 34. Starting tolerance may cause a second drive to read the bits left by the first drive (Fig. 35).

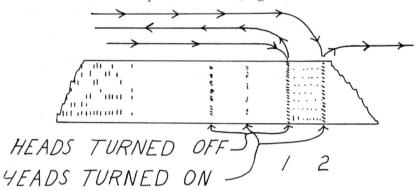

HEADS TURNED OFF

HEADS TURNED ON      1    2

**Fig. 36—WRITE BACKSPACE READ THEN WRITE.** Here are two types of noise in the inter-record gap. The splashes on the left are due to the write heads turning off and then on. The wide splash between "1" and "2" is the failure to erase all previous data and having a slightly different tracking than previously. At "1" the erase head is turned off. At "2" the erase head is turned on.

Variation in stopping distance can leave great amounts of noise in the gap. In the example shown in Figure 36, many bits can be left in the gap. Assuming the drive A has written a long record. Drive B then overwrites and stops at location 1, generating an inter-record gap. Now drive B backspaces and re-reads the record and stops at location 2. This variation in stopping location is not intentional but is part of the stopping tolerance. The information between 1 and 2 has not been erased. The erase heads were not on, as the record was being re-read. This collection of non-erased data looks just like Figure 34. And it can cause the same problem.

Many drive systems get around this problem by erasing forward a few tenths of an inch before backspacing. Thus the system insures that the entire tape will be erased no matter what the read-stopping tolerance is.

Erasing tape just before rewriting has another purpose. Write current switches faster when it switches to magnetizing with the direction of existing tape magnetization. Thus the exact location of current switch could be varied by the previous history of the tape. Erasing the tape in one direction just before writing, makes the point of current switch predictable and consistent.

**summary**

The tape drive must guide on the edge of the tape to control the lateral location of the tape as it passes over the heads. These edge guides should be hard enough to stand the constant abrasion of the tape. Guiding about the head must also eliminate any flap which may develop as a result of starting and stopping. Failure in either function will result in read or write errors. Improper edge guiding can damage tape.

An erase head relieves the tolerance demands on a drive. The erase head tends to make up for inaccuracies in the guiding and in starting and stopping distances. Erasing tape completely before rewriting, makes data more interchangeable and eliminates tape noise.

## CHAPTER 5. Questions

1. Why is tape edge guided near the head?
2. What is tape flap? How can it be prevented?
3. What are the benefits of an erase head?

# 6 electronics

THIS CHAPTER IS NOT A DESIGNER'S HANDBOOK on how to design tape drive controllers. Rather it is an introduction to the problems that tape drives present to the controller. And conversely, what effect does the controller have on the mechanical operation of the drive? The material in this chapter would be equally good for tube, transistor, or cryogenic controllers. Specific means of generating the timing pulses in the controller is left open. The chapter introduces the reader to that big expensive box referred to alternately as the controller, synchronizer, channel, or interface unit.

## what is the control designed to do?

A tape drive is much like a car. Both have capabilities, reliabilities, and certain limits. Neither one by itself is very useful. Both need detailed direction and control. In a car, we call this the driver (or the backseat driver). In a tape drive we call this direction the controller.

It is the controller's job to accept general commands from the computer and break these down into detailed, specific instructions. The computer says *Read*. The controller interprets this to the drive as: (1) start moving tape forward, (2) time out 3.2 MS, and (3) start looking for data, etc.

In addition it is frequently the controller's job to match the speed of the tape drive to the speed of the computer. The computer will issue a command in a few micro-seconds, but it will take the tape drive many milli-seconds to execute the command. The controller then has to insure that the computer doesn't come back with a second command to override the first one.

## timing from the drive

The biggest single job the controller has is timing. More than half of the controller is taken up with timing. The timing job is divided into two sections—the timing necessary to control the transfer of data, and that which is necessary because of the movements of the tape drive.

Data transfer timers work in the microsecond or nano-second region. Motion timers work in the millisecond region.

There are two principal means to estimate time. One is digital. The pulses from a crystal oscillator clock are counted to indicate that a certain time has passed. The second means is analog. The time that it takes the energy in a capacitor or in an inductor to run down is an indication of passing time. Most controllers use both methods of telling time. Many controllers use the digital means for determining the time of character gates, record gates, and read-or-write delays. But universally, delay lines, inductors, and capacitors are used to correct the skew timing of the read-or-write heads. The type of timing device used depends on cost and the accuracy required.

## motion control timing for writing

When the CPU issues a command to *write,* the controller will tell some drive to move tape. The command will take place in a matter of microseconds if it is a normal operation. The time between **A** and **B** on Figure 37 is used by the tape drive to move a pinch roller or to

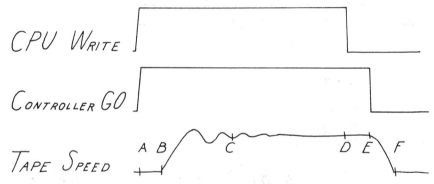

**Fig. 37—WRITE OPERATION.** These graphs demonstrate what happens on a CPU write command. The time between "A" and "B" is used to get the tape engaged with a rotating capstan. The time "B" to "C" is spent getting the tape up to speed and waiting for the speed variations to settle out. Data writing tape takes place between "C" and "D". Between "D" and "E" the tape drive controller is waiting to see if the CPU will issue a second command, and also the controller is keeping the tape up to speed so that a read check can be completed. The tape is stopped between "E" and "F".

switch an air valve. At **B** the tape starts to move. Tape will come up to speed and oscillate about the steady state speed. At some point **C,** the speed variation will be less than the speed variation specified, and writing can take place. The controller determines the location of point **C** by timing from **A** to **C.** Typical values are between 2 and 5 MS. At point **C** the controller allows data from the CPU to be written on tape.

This writing continues until point **D** when all the data is written. The motion command will be continued to the drive until at least point **E**. At this time, the read head has passed over the data and tape motion can be stopped. However, many controllers continue the motion command until point **F**. There are two principal reasons for doing this. First, the controller is giving the CPU time to come back with a second *write* command before tape motion is halted. If a second *write* command is issued before tape is halted, many drives will go through the inter-record gap much faster. The second reason for continuing the tape motion for a time is that the next command may be a *backspace*. If the next command is a *backspace,* the controller wants to insure that the drive is far enough forward to insure that the last record can be re-read. If the tape read head is too close to the data, the read delay may blank out some information while the drive is just getting up to speed.

## motion control timing for reading

When the CPU issues a *read* command, the controller will tell some drive to move tape. This will also take place in a matter of microseconds if it is a normal operation. In a similar manner to writing,

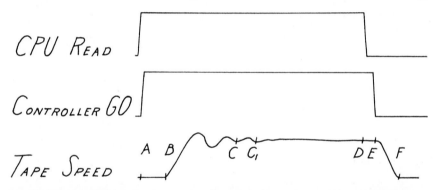

**Fig. 38—READ OPERATION.** These graphs demonstrate what happens on a CPU read command. The time between "A" and "B" is used to get the tape engaged with a rotating capstan. The time between "B" and "C" is spent getting the tape up to speed and allowing speed variations to settle out. At "C" writing could take place, but the read head is located behind the write head so that reading will not take place until "$C_1$". Between "$C_1$" and "D" reading takes place. The controller is looking for a second read command between "D" and "E". The tape drive is then stopped between "E" and "F".

the drive requires the time between **A** and **B** to move actuators or valves (Fig. 38). At point **C**, the controller allows data to be read from tape. Up to this time, the controller assumes that any data read from the tape is noise in the gap. Data will not start moving to the CPU at point **C.** This is just the point at which the controller allows data to flow to the CPU if it is available. The actual time of the start of data transfer is dependent on data location. If the drive is consistent, the time between **A** and **C1** will be the same as the time **A** to **C** in Figure 37. Thus, data will be read at point **C1** in Figure 38. The controller timing between **A** and **C** for a *read* must be less than it is for a *write*. A *read* delay is generally 50 to 60 percent of a *write* delay. This difference in delay allows a fast starting drive to read data written by a slow starter.

Reading will continue until point **D** in Figure 38. At this time there is no more data on tape. The motion command to the tape may be continued until point **E.** This may be done in order to give the CPU more time to issue a second *read* command. If a drive can start to stop, and respond to a second *read* command with no lost time, the delay between **D** and **E** is not needed.

## read backspace after a read

When a controller is given the command to backspace, a different sequence of events should take place depending on whether the drive read or wrote the last record. First, let's consider the simpler case.

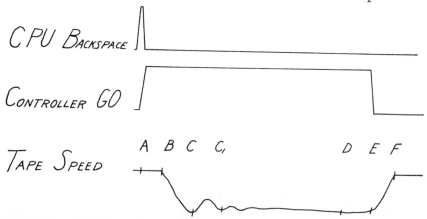

**Fig. 39—BACKSPACE.** A back space operation is really a read in reverse. Data may or may not be sent to the CPU. Time "A" to "B" is tape capstan engagement time. At "C" the controller starts looking for data. Time "B" to "C" is not the same for a backspace and for a read. In a backspace the read head is the closest head to the reverse data. The data may not come until "C₁". Data is read between "C₁" and "D". The delay "D" to "E" is long enough to insure that the write and erase head get over the data too.

Backspace after reading a record. This command is described as if data were not being transferred to the CPU during the backspace. Whether this takes place has no effect on the tape motion controls.

The data must be read by the controller to determine where the beginning of the record is. Sending the data to the CPU will not place much additional burden on the controllers. In Figure 39, CPU command is issued at **A**. Within microseconds the controller has issued a tape move command to the drive. A normal startup delay is encountered between **A** and **B**. Some drives require much longer startup

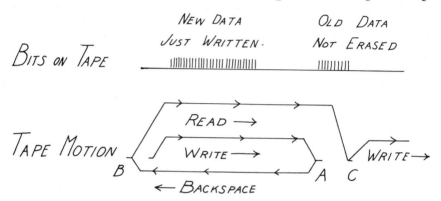

**Fig. 40—WRITE BACKSPACE READ AND WRITE (WRONG).** This demonstrates how stopping tolerance can cause the old data to be skipped by erase head. The first stop was at "A". The backspace was at stop "B". The second forward stop was at "C" due to stopping tolerance.

delay in the reverse direction. This is caused by the need of the mechanism to change direction from forward to reverse. Most drives need no more time between **A** and **B** than they do in the forward direction. At point **C** the controller allows data to be read from tape. Point **C** is located by timing from **A**. The length of time may be the same as a read delay. Data will be read from tape at **C1**. Where **C1** occurs in relation to **C** is dependent on reverse startup characteristics, and the stop delay **D** to **E** in Figure 38. Data will be read until point **D** in Figure 39. This point is determined by the amount of data on tape. The controller then continues tape motion until **E** and causes the tape to stop. The delay between point **D** and **E** is more than a normal stopping delay. With most digital drives, the write head is still back in the record when the end of data sensed is in backspace. So there is some time needed just to get the write head out of the data area. (The write head is not used during backspace.) Beyond this, the erase head may be further back in the data than the write head is. (The erase head is not being used either.)

Also, most systems allow more room for starting than they do for stopping. The principal reason for this is that the tape speed is given time to settle down before reading or writing takes place. Hence, the start distance is longer than stop distance. The reverse stop delay must take into account the location of the write and erase heads, and the need to have a longer start distance than stop distance.

## backspace after a write

Backspacing after a *write* command is different from backspacing after a *read* command. The difference is caused by a desire to prevent noise in the gap. Suppose that a backspace after a write were the same as after a read. Figure 40 illustrates what can happen if stopping tolerance varies. A new block of data is written and the drive stops with the write head at **A** and the erase head at **A1.** The erase head is turned off and the drive is backspaced to **B.** If now the CPU gives a command to read, the drive may go forward to position **C.** The tape drive takes the erase head to position **C** not by intention, but by accident. Normal stopping tolerance causes the longer stop. The distance between **A** and **C** is 0.01 inches or less. Now when a write command is given, the write heads will be turned on and the drive will move forward. Thus a piece of the old data block between **A** and **C** will be left unerased. Noise at **A** is left in the inter-record gap due to the turning of write heads. This "noise in the gap" can cause errors.

In order to prevent this type of "noise" a different sequence should be followed for a backspace after a write than is followed for a backspace after a read (Fig. 41). When the controller recognizes that the

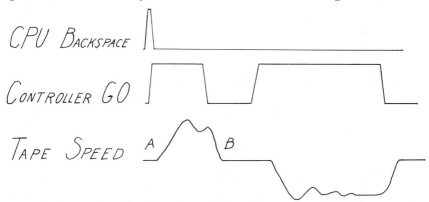

**Fig. 41—WRITE BACKSPACE READ AND WRITE (RIGHT).** This demonstrates the correct backspace operation from a written status. First the tape is moved forward "A" to "B", then a normal backspace takes place. The distance "A" to "B" is great enough to insure that stopping tolerance does not cause the non-erasing of any data.

drive previously has written, the controller will not cause the tape to go backwards immediately. First the controller will move the tape forward. The distance the drive moves forward is not critical. It must be enough to insure that any part of an old record is not skipped by stopping tolerance and write heads are turned off far enough forward so the turn-off noise gets erased. This means that the distance from **A** to **B** must be greater than any possible stopping tolerance. After the erase forward is accomplished, the remainder of the backspace is like a *backspace after read.* The timing necessary to cause the drive to move forward from **A** to **B** is a unique time. There is no other timer

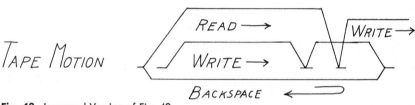

Fig. 42—Improved Version of Fig. 40.

like it in the controller. Therefore, most controllers use the normal write delay timers. This makes the distance from **A** to **B** much greater than it needs to be, but it is cheaper this way. Figure 42 shows the improved version of Figure 40.

### skip forward

A skip forward command has become necessary because of the higher recording densities. As recording densities went from 200 bits per inch to 556 bits per inch, defects in the tape became evident. (Tape manufacturers have made mighty strides to reduce these errors to zero.) When these errors developed, some means were needed to get over them. One way is to write a no account record. This record says "Don't use this record in your processing." However, other manufacturers don't want to do this because they fear that the data will come in so garbled that the message can't be read. This record may not be recognized as a no account record. The CPU program would then have to stop because of an unreadable record.

To avoid this, a *skip* command is used. A *skip* command generates a very long inter-record gap. The tape drive is caused to go into the write mode and erase tape for three to nine inches. When tape is read, the CPU will never know that a bad piece of tape existed. The CPU will not know about the bad tape unless the program measures the time between issuance of a read and the arrival of data. The data laid down after an erase will come in much later than the data laid down after a normal gap. A skip command then trades off computer time against the longer use of tape. At some point, when the tape has developed "x" number of bad spots, it is cheaper to throw away the tape than hold up the computer while passing over the bad tape. This "x" number will, of course, vary greatly depending on the cost of the computer and the cost of tape.

As a quick example, $100-an-hour computer cost is about three cents per second. Suppose that on the average, a tape must be reused about 10 times once it is mounted on a reel hub. (It must be read 10 times because data will be written which will be read 10 times. Or, once mounted the reel is to be used in a sort routine which will require ten passes, etc.) The question then is how many bad spots can the tape have before the reel should not be mounted due to the cost of time. A reel of tape costs about $40. Dividing three cents per second into $40 tells us the computer can waste 1,300 seconds on this tape before it should be junked. However, we are going to reuse the tape 10 times once it is mounted, so the computer can waste 130 seconds per pass. At 75 inches-per-second tape speed, this is 9,700 inches or 800 feet, or 2,800 skip spots. This is a lot of bad spots.

Other considerations may alter the number of bad spots tolerated. The computer may cost more than $100 per hour. The tape may be used more often than 10 times once it is mounted on a hub to be rewritten. If the data is to be written for a long term store, it may be desirable not to write on tape that is in any way approaching the end of life. There are many good reasons why this formula should not be followed closely. But it gives us a starting point for deciding when to throw tape away.

One last point—many scientific installations use only the first hundred feet of tape for one program. These installations may pass over the first hundred feet 5,000 times in the course of the program. Since these installations know that all the bad spots are concentrated in the first hundred feet, they may tear off the first hundred feet when the program is finished. This is one case where the tape is thrown away in little pieces.

## rewind timing

The timing for a rewind command is so dependent on the particular drive that it is impossible to generalize. One drive must raise the head and pull tape out of the columns; another drive must retract the buffer arms and start the reel motors slowly; still another drive must put the capstan motor into high speed, etc. One thing is common in rewind. As far as I know, all rewind is done off-line without holding up the computer. Usually a relay is picked up and held all during the time of a rewind. For a 2,400-foot reel rewind time may be anything from 0.9 to 7.5 minutes. Generally the faster drives have the faster rewind. The controller generally is not tied up with rewind either, as the computer may be working with other tape drives on the same controller.

There is some timing in the drive itself for rewind. It is not necessary that this timing be accurate, and it generally isn't. The drive usually watches the machine reel and the beginning of tape reflective spot. When either one of these indications say rewind is about over, the drive puts the brakes on. This may complete the rewind, or more slow speed backup may be needed. The timing in the drive is closely associated with the hardware and is designed to service the hardware needs.

### data timing

The timing of data from tape to the computer is a high-speed operation. The timing pulses may be ten times faster than the data coming off tape. This may be easier to understand if we think of the data from tape as being a line of soldiers three feet apart. If we want to check on the soldiers, we must have a ruler which is marked off in increments smaller than three feet. Otherwise, half the soldiers will be farther apart than three feet and the rest of the soldiers will be closer together than three feet. A ruler marked off in inches will allow us to say, if the soldier is three feet plus or minus one inch, he is O.K. So it is with data from tape. In order to check the data from tape we must allow a tolerance, and this tolerance demands a higher-speed operation than the data from tape.

There are a number of ways that digital data can be recorded on tape. The most common way is to record seven bits and depend on an *OR* clock to bring the data back in. Other systems record a clock bit for every character that is recorded. Still other systems record a clock for every bit that is written. In the following description, the *OR* clock system will be described. This is the IBM and ASA means of recording on half-inch tape. It is by far the most widely used system. After the *OR* clock system, other systems will be described.

### writing

Writing on tape is a marvel of simplicity. But to write well requires the best talent, the most exact time, and the closest control possible. Let's start off simply and write simply (see Figs. 43A and 43B). This is a picture we have seen many times before. It is a magnetic write head, magnetizing tape north to south, left to right. Notice how the direction of current in the write head causes the flux lines in tape to

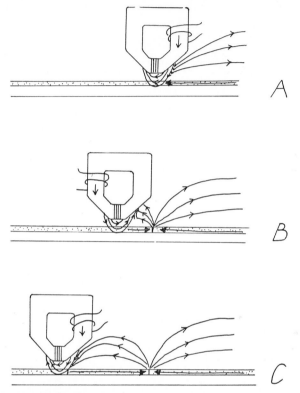

**Fig. 43A**—FLUX PATTERNS ON WRITING. This series demonstrates how flux passes through the write head and through tape during the writing of a one bit. In "A" the flux lines that follow the write head are those resulting from the magnetization of tape. In "B" and "C" this flux reversal will be sensed by the read head. The arrows in the head shows the forced direction of flux due to write current.

be north to south, right to left. When the current in the write head is reversed, the tape is magnetized south to north, left to right. And where this transition occurs, there is a north pole facing a north pole. The resulting flux pattern is shown in the third section of Figure 43A. Right at the junction of the two north poles, flux is caused to be at right angles to the surface of the tape. This is called a *bit* on tape. Depending on the system, we may read a zero bit or a one bit or a clock bit. But we have written and read on tape. Wasn't that simple?

## what can go wrong?

There are many things that can go wrong with the process to keep from writing well. In order to understand them, let's jump right into a seven-track system and see what the requirements are (Fig. 44).

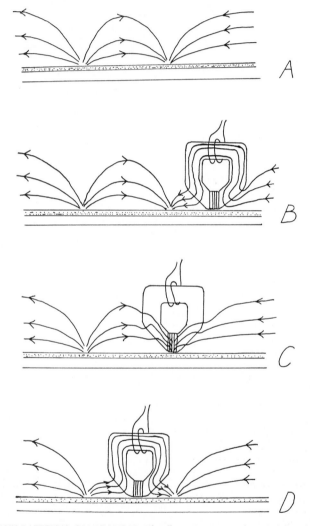

**Fig. 43B—FLUX PATTERNS ON READING.** The flux patterns in the read head are demonstrated in these four sections: "A" Flux from tape undisturbed. "B" The flux passes through the read head as it approaches the south pole on the tape. "C" When the head is directly over a bit of tape there is little or no flux through the head. This is because of the opposing flux pattern at a bit location. The voltage in the read head is maximum not because of the flux (there isn't any in the head) but because the rate of change of flux is maximum. "D" Flux in the head has completely reversed and is stable.

If data is written at 1,000 frames per inch, each frame is 0.001 inch apart or 1,000 microinches between frames. In order to keep one frame from getting mixed up with the next frame, the frame must be laid down squarely enough that the bit doesn't overlap for the worst cases (dashed line **A** in Fig. 44). Because the character gate in an OR

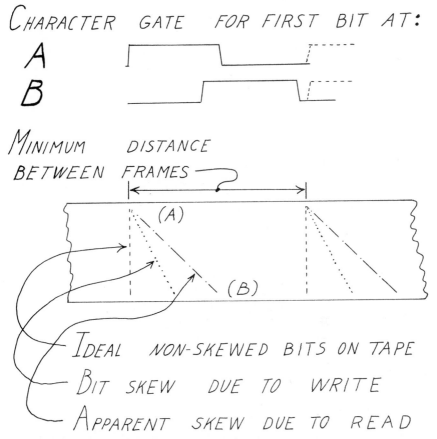

CHARACTER GATE FOR FIRST BIT AT:

A

B

MINIMUM DISTANCE BETWEEN FRAMES

(A)

(B)

IDEAL NON-SKEWED BITS ON TAPE

BIT SKEW DUE TO WRITE

APPARENT SKEW DUE TO READ

**Fig. 44—BIT SKEW ON TAPE.** This drawing illustrates the bit skew on tape. The character gate "A" is started by a bit located with skew near "A" on tape. The character gate "B" would be started by a bit on tape having skew like that at "B" on tape. The character gate can be started early or late. Since the next character gate may start early, frame density must allow a twice the worst skew between frames.

clock system can begin on the last bit in the frame, the distance from the last bit of one frame to the first bit on the next frame must be equal to or greater than the worst possible skew. This means that the data must be square within 500 microinches or one-half of 1,000 microinches between frames. Since the reading head can be different from the writing head, it should be allowed one-half the available tolerance. Thus, we must be square within 250 microinches when writing.

This number can be further reduced by consideration of speed variations, pulse crowding, and other nasty little factors. But we have reduced it enough for our present purpose.

What can cause the writing outside of our 250 microinch tolerance? Time and distance. The time when the heads are switched can cause the data to be out of the 250 microinch tolerance. The deviation of the head gaps from a perfect right angle can cause writing to be out of tolerance. Mechanical head tolerance and guiding tolerance may be as much as 150 microinches. This leaves 100 microinches for variation in the electronics.

The current in the two coils in Figure 43A does not shut off instantaneously. It takes some time for one coil to shut off and the next coil to start to conduct. Suppose it takes 0.5 usec; this may seem like a long time when electronic pulses of 0.3 usec are used in many of today's computers. But remember these currents must go up to the write heads, which contain nickel iron. The inductance of the head and the distance the current must travel may limit turn-on and turn-off speed. In a 0.5 usec, tape moving at 150 inches per second equals 75 microinches. The inductance of the head winding may vary; the distance of the tape from the head may vary, which in turn, varies head induction. The driving voltage may vary so that the switching time varies. The individual head-write circuits may be faster or slower than other parallel circuits in turning on or off. All these factors add up to make the time of switching uncertain with a 100 microinch or 0.75 usec. Mechanical head tolerance and electronic write variation can add up to more than 250 microinches. To keep all these tolerances correct is the job of good write electronics, which means good writing.

## head deskewing

In the previous paragraphs, it has been pointed out that there are two causes of skew bits on tape: mechanical head tolerances, and variation in the time of switching. We also may see that these two can be made to work against one another to cancel out. Thus, if the mechanical tolerance of the head tends to cause a bit to be written toward the beginning of the tape, the time of switching that write head can be delayed so that the bit is not written so far toward the beginning of tape. This process of correcting mechanical tolerances with electrical delays is called deskewing. Drives that work above 500 frames per inch must use some deskewing.

Deskewing is generally done with delay lines. Delay lines are prepackaged inductances and capacitances which cause electrical pulses to be delayed from 0.2 to 5.0 usec. Connection is made to the delay desired. Figure 45 shows three frames written on tape. The first frame

*S*KE W ON TAPE DUE TO:

1) HEAD CURVE & ALIGNMENT

2) DYNAMIC MOVEMENT OF TAPE

3) DYNAMIC CHANGE OF WRITE CIRCUITS

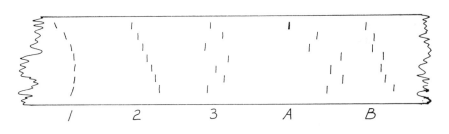

A) *S*UMMATION OF SKEWS *1, 2, 3*

B) *A*FTER SKEW CORRECTION

**Fig. 45—BIT SKEW PATTERNS.** This demonstrates the principal factor of skew on tape. Frame "A" is the combined skews of 1, 2, and 3. Frame 1 is lead skew only. Frame 2 is dynamic skew only. Frame 3 is random electrical skew only. Frame "B" is after deskew.

1 is written with only the head tolerance causing skew. Bits will normally fall into an arc because the head manufacturing lapping process causes this pattern. The second frame 2 represents the skew that is written on tape due to dynamic skew alone. Dynamic skew is due to the movement of the tape during writing. It can only be corrected by straighter tape and better guiding. The third frame 3 is caused by the random electrical timing skew. Head drives are not uniform in their switching because of variation in write voltages and variation in inductance of the head. That part of the skew which is not consistent can only be eliminated at the source, by eliminating the inconsistency. Cross talk must be eliminated. The drive voltage must be made stable.

This frame **A** represents the total effects of all skew. The bits are skewed due to head, dynamic, and electrical tolerance. This is the worst skew condition on tape. In the last frame **B**, delay lines have been introduced which delayed the writing of those pulses which would have occurred too soon. Electronic cross-talk is reduced. This frame is de-skewed. A closer look at the last frame will tell us that there is some skew left. The line of bits written on tape is not perfect. As in life, a perfect line is impossible. There are reasons for this. The choosing of the proper delay is made after the skew is measured. Measurements are not perfect, so the choice of a delay line will not be perfect. Also delay lines are normally discontinuous. They are tapped every 0.25 usec. For example, delays are possible which are perhaps 0.25 usec, 0.50, 0.75 and so forth. If our head requires a delay which is 0.40, we will choose 0.50 and slightly overcorrect the error. Also, electronic cross-talk cannot be eliminated, only reduced. Dynamic skew cannot be eliminated completely. It can only be improved with better guiding

### cross-talk

Unfortunately, the way in which electronics is implemented and the data which is written may cause skew. The electronic-caused and data-caused skew should be completely eliminated, but it takes very detailed and careful design. To illustrate how difficult it is to get all the electronic skew out, one example will be given.

Figure 46 is a three-track system. All mechanical and electrical compensations have been made so that three bits are written on tape as nearly perfectly as possible. The first frames show this deskew writing.

**Fig. 46—RESULTS OF CROSS TALK.** The frame on the left is perfectly written. The next frame is written with identical circuits but with only two bits written instead of three.

Next, only the **B** and **C** bits were written. And **B** and **C** were not lined up. In order to understand what happened, let's look at what was being done. The head being used looked like that in Figure 47. Time delays were needed in Track **A** and **C** to line these up with Track **B**. The actual timing of the switch of the write heads is shown in Figure 47. Track **A** and **B** have mechanical skew and are switched first to compensate. Track **B** is the base and it is switched last.

Unknown to designers, Track **A** was causing Track **B** to switch earlier than it should. The designers did not know this and put in more delay to compensate for the induction from **A** to **B**. When **A** was not written, the cross track induction was not there, but the delay was. Therefore **B** was written later, as shown in Figure 46.

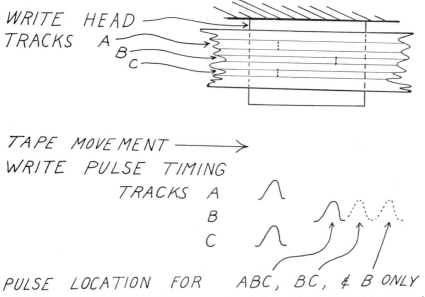

**Fig. 47**—CROSS TALK CAUSED SKEW. This demonstrates how three write pulses are timed to correct for the mechanical head skew. However, "A" and "C" have an effect on "B". "B" time of writing is dependent on when and if "A" and "C" are written. Thus, the write pulse for "B" could be at three places.

It was found that the cross-track induction signal was carried up through the power supply and back into Track **B** circuits. There are many ways spurious signals can cause skew. What is important to understand is that tape-writing systems have to work as systems, with random bit patterns. The writing system has to work over a range of temperature, and it must be stable with time. This type of electronic system design approaches the very best that electronic engineers can do at this time. Good write circuits are not easy to come by.

## longitudinal redundancy check character (LRC)

The LRC character is a natural in the NRZI method of writing. (NRZI is a system of writing on magnetic material. In this system, magnetic flux does not return to zero, and a flux reversal indicates a one bit.) The LRC is the last character written and it almost comes free. As data is written on tape the write heads are switched back and forth. In truth, they are keeping a binary count of the bits as they are recorded on tape. After all the data from the CPU is written, the write heads are saturating tape in some pattern depending on what count of bits were written in each track. Therefore, if the write heads are reset to their original direction, a character will be written. A bit will be written wherever the total number of bits in a track is odd. A bit will not be written where the total number of bits in a track is even. This pattern of bits constitutes a character which is a longitudinal redundancy check of the record.

A little playing with bit patterns will demonstrate that the vertical redundancy check bit will be correct for the LRC character whenever even character parity is used. This is not true when the data is written with odd character parity. One other point, the LRC character may be all zeros, or not exist.

## cyclic redundancy check character (crc)

The LRC check character has a serious weakness. If an even number of bits are dropped in one track, the LRC will not recognize the drop out. Immediately I can hear from the peanut gallery, "But if you drop bits in one track, the vertical check bit will detect the error." In general this is true. But it is not true in all cases. For example, assume a record on magnetic tape like, "0000055477 Joe Taunt etc." If the tape drive fails to read the first two or four characters of this record, the LRC will not detect the error. The LRC keeps a binary count of the bits in each track, and the loss of an even number of the same character, (zeros in this case), will not disturb the binary count. And of course, there is no vertical error when the entire character is lost. Other combinations of character loss at the beginning or end of a record are possible without detection. Such failure to read the beginning or end of a record is possible by a single malfunction. A record gate opening too late, or closing too soon will give the condition.

In order to check for this error, several companies have developed a cyclic redundancy check character. This check character is similar to an LRC. However an LRC takes a binary count of all the bits in one track. A CRC takes a binary count of the bits in the record diagonally through the record. A bit in a track of frame one is added to the bit in the next track of frame two and so forth. This diagonal binary addition is done for all tracks. After the diagonal count goes across all tracks, it continues in the first track. Therefore the count is cyclic. This type of checking insures that the loss of an even number of characters on the beginning or at the end, will be detected. Every bit in every character is checked in three ways. 1. In the vertical redundance check, or character parity. 2. In the LRC check, or longitudinal parity, and 3. In the CRC or cyclic parity.

IBM has added some additional features to the idea of cyclic check character. By inverting certain bits, (making ones into zeros, and zeroes into ones), the chance of error is further reduced, and one bits are caused to be included in the LRC in all cases. The IBM version of the CRC is being made a part of the ASA standard for magnetic tape recording at 800 bits per inch density.

## reading

Many of the problems that exist in writing are also present in reading. For example, the read head has the same skew problem that a write head has. Delay lines are also used to deskew or compensate for the mechanical skew of the head. However, many of the problems that exist in writing do not exist in reading. The example under the writing discussion demonstrated that high power levels cause crosstrack induction, and that voltage levels could cause skew. All signals in reading are very normal electronic levels without any large switch of energy to cause cross talk.

The signals that are read off the read head are in the 1 to 15 millivolt region. This is a low signal and electrical noise is a problem.

One of the most difficult problems in read circuits is to determine just when the signal bits are in. Data that is written on tape is not read off with the same time pattern as it was written. Besides the reading head skew, there is a problem of pulse crowding. Pulse crowding means that the magnetic flux from one bit is affecting the flux field of a second bit. This problem and means of correction are well written up in the literature. See IEEE (formerly IRE) Transaction on Electronic Computers for many fine articles on magnetic recording and read-back.

Since the data from tape is received in a skewed manner, the read system must line it up. The line-up process is just like getting a bunch of kids together. The first child to arrive has to wait for a period of time until it is likely that all the kids coming are present. Then all the kids are taken together to the activity. The bits from the tape are handled in the same way. The bits are made to wait in flip-flops until a character gate says that all the bits for that character are probably there. Then all the bits are shipped over to the computer as a character. With kids and bits it is possible that one last straggler will want in after the gate is closed. The answer should be the same: "Too bad, you're late. You can't go with this group." A late bit causes errors.

## character gates

In order for the controller to know that all the bits are together from one character, the controller must develop a time which can be called the character gate. This time will be long enough so that all the bits for one character get together in a register, but the gate will be short enough to prevent any stray bits belonging to other characters from entering (Fig. 48). Choosing the proper length of time is critical. The factors which control the length of time are: (1) noncorrected static skew, (2) dynamic skew, and (3) method of starting the character gate timer. Static skew is the skew caused because the read and write heads are not straight and square. Dynamic skew is the skew caused by the electronics, speed variation in the drive, and the movement of the tape. The method of starting the character gate is frequently controlled by the format of data on tape.

In most IBM compatible half-inch systems, an *OR* clock is used. An *OR* clock is one which is started by the first bit sensed: this one, *OR* that one. Whichever bit comes in first starts the character gate. This type of clocking is simple and reliable, but it has one disadvantage—the timing of the character gate is dependent on the data. As the data varies, so does the timing.

## record gate

After all characters are formed and sent to the CPU, it is necessary that the controller know when a record or data block is completed

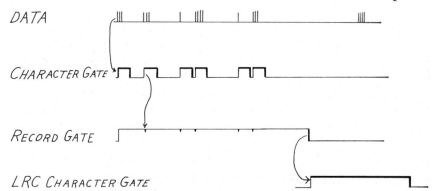

**Fig. 48—GATING DURING READING.** These drawings demonstrate the possible variation in read gates. The Record gate and LRC gate are dependent on the Character gate.

(Fig. 48). Most systems are variable in length records. The normal way the controller determines that a record is completed is to watch character gates and wait for them to go away. Thus a record gate timer starts timing at the end of every character gate. That is, if another character gate doesn't reset the timer, the timer runs out and says "end of record." The engineers in one company refer to this means of timing as the "caboose detector." When there are no more boxcars coming along, you know it must be the caboose passing.

## LRC gate

It was described in the section on Writing that an LRC character is written after all data is written (Fig. 48). This check character comes as a result of resetting the write drives. The timing of the LRC character is not critical. It usually is set off by four character pitches from the rest of the data in the block. A LRC gate is started as soon as the record gate is closed. This LRC gate stays up until the LRC character is in and then it also closes. The fall of the LRC gate signals the completion of the timing necessary to read a record.

## other timing

After the fall of the LRC gate, there are other timings that are made. However these timings have to do with the motion control of the drive. The timing frequently has to do with waiting to see if the CPU will send another command, or the timings are insuring that the drive moves far enough into the inter-record gap to give proper operation, etc.

## clock systems of writing

A clock system of writing is a system that writes a timing clock on tape. This clock bit is used to tell the controller that another character is coming and starts a character gate. It was pointed out under the OR clock system that any bit that arrives may be the bit that starts the character gate. This bit might be the one with the most skew, so that the character gate is started off with maximum possible skew timing. In a clock bit system, the clock bit is always there and it has been written with a controlled amount of skew. When the clock bit is read, its relation to the rest of the data is known; the character gate timing is generated. Figure 49 shows the character gates that are generated from skewed data. Notice how the OR clock gates vary because of their different starting points. The clock bit gates vary not at all. The regularity of the clock bit gates is the reason that a system using clock bits can be written at twice the density of an OR clock system. For the price of writing one more track of clocks on tape, twice the density of recording is possible. Work on generating a variable frequency clock has been done to generate a pseudo clock-track.

## phase recording

There are a number of systems of phase recordings. Phase recording is a system of recording where each track of bits is self clocking. A clock is written right along with the data on every track. Sometimes a

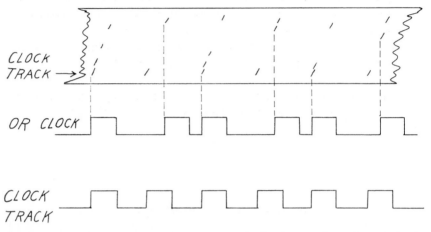

**Fig. 49**—COMPARISON OF "OR" AND BIT CLOCKS. This drawing shows the variation in character gates that result from ORing the data bits from tape. If the clock track is used the character gates is regular. Clock bit character gates can be spaced closer together because of the regularity (higher bit density). A pseudo clock bit will approach the benefits of a clock bit on tape.

clock bit is written at regular intervals, and the presence or absence of bits between the clocks indicates a one bit or a zero bit. In other systems, the clock bit is written only if the data requires a flux change. Up-flux is one, down-flux is zero. These systems have a big advantage. A single track of data can be read and recognized for what it is, independent of the data on other tracks. Hence a character gate for the data off tape is meaningless. Generally, the data is stored in a character shift register until all the bits from one character have been assembled. Then the character is formed and shipped to the CPU. This type of recording allows much higher densities of recording. And the system is much more tolerant of skew. Recording at 2,000 frames per inch is reasonable with this recording technique.

One big problem—loss of data in one track makes the remainder of the record nonrecoverable unless error correction codes are used. However, phase recording is a very reliable system.

## in summary

The controller must generate certain timings to control the motion of the tape drive and to control the flow of data. The timings that are used in tape motion control are in the millisecond region. For the most part these are the timings of delay to allow the mechanism to perform some function. The timings that are associated with reading and writing are in the microsecond region. The timings in writing are for spacing the data properly on tape, and for compensating for the mechanical skew of the head. The timing associated with reading is to compensate for the mechanical skew of the head and to determine when the data that is arriving from tape should be considered a complete character or record. Three general types of character clocking are *OR* clock, recorded or pseudo-clock bit, and phase recording.

The means of generating the timing are of no significance to a user. Analog, capacitor and inductor discharge, and digital (counting the pulses from a crystal clock) are used. Both analog and digital techniques are used to establish timing. Either or both systems are good.

## CHAPTER 6. Questions

1. What is the purpose of the electronic controller?
2. What are the two techniques of generating timing?
3. Describe how data is written on tape.
4. How does a character become skewed?
5. How can a drive compensate for skew?
6. List four causes of skew.
7. What is the function of Character, Record, or Longitudinal Check gates?
8. What is phase or clock recording?

# 7 operator controls and human factors

IN THESE DAYS OF TAPE LOADED PROGRAMS, off-line media conversion, and simple console routines, the loading and unloading of tape drives is the only manual operation holding up the computers. A simple stop watch told one user that 40 percent of his CPU time was spent waiting to load or unload drives. Every second saved in loading is 3 cents' worth of computer time.

Each drive requires certain buttons and lights. These are needed to give the operator control of the drive, to give him confidence that the drive is operating properly, and to speed up his work with the drive. One manufacturer released a drive with two buttons on it, *off-line* and *on-line*. Functionally, these two are all that is required. Depressing the *off-line* button gives the operator complete control of the drive. An *on-line* button gives the computer complete control. However, these controls were not enough.

Whenever a drive didn't work, the program had to be modified to change an address. The drives did not have a simple selector, or indicator switch, which could be used to change all the commands from this drive to some other. The program had to be changed each time a drive address was changed. As you may guess, many times the program address was changed incorrectly. After a few thousand wild gyrations the computer program had to be reloaded, then remodified. All this reloading took place at a computer cost of $100 an hour. Tape drive selector switches can save time and money. Executive software routines do reduce the need for select switches.

One computer user thought it so important for the operators to see the lights on each and every drive that he set up a number of mirrors. These mirrors allowed the operator at the console to see every drive in the computer room. He could even see the drives behind a post! Lights on a drive pay off. They cause the operator to investigate faults sooner.

Feedback can be defined as the transfer of information from the output to the input. This definition will be applied to the operator

**90**

machine system. The input is the operator pushing a button, closing a door, or releasing a catch. The output is a light turning on, a tape reel moving, or the computer starting to process. Whenever an operator pushes a button, closes a door, or does nothing, as a result of computer lights coming on or tapes moving, feedback is working. Feedback causes the operator to do something or nothing as a result of what he sees or hears in the computer operation.

Tape drive feedback is important to management because it causes operators to take faster corrective action. Faster corrective action means more computer operation per day, and lower cost per operation.

## buttons and lights

What controls are needed? Even the manufacturer who released the drive with two buttons agreed that a drive needs an *on-line* and *off-line* button. The operator must be able to push a button and know that the computer no longer has control of the drive. This will make the operation swifter because there is no doubt in the operator's mind that "Maybe this thing will start up all by itself." To feed back the feeling of confidence to the operator faster, a light should be associated with the *off-line* and *on-line* buttons. This light, frequently labeled *ready*, positively indicates to the operator that either the computer has control or he does. The light is also used by the console operator. If a program is hung in a loop waiting, the non-illuminated *ready* light will tell him from fifty feet that a drive is not ready.

Once the operator has control, the most frequent operation will be unloading and loading tape reels. Most of the time, the first thing that has to be done is to unload the reel that is on the drive. This requres that the operator either push the unload button or manually open up the drive. Between the two, there is little that can be said as far as speed is concerned. Both the electrical unload and the mechanical openings are quite fast. After the drive is unloaded—not demounted—the file reel must be turned by hand to take up the last few feet of tape onto the file reel. Most reels have a brake which must be released during the unload. A button or switch should release the brake. The button must be convenient so that manual reel turning is possible.

After the old reel is put away, the operator must put a new reel on the hub and tighten up the hub. Note the operating level of the reels. Are the reels at a height that is convenient for an operator? If the operating height is wrong, your operators are going to be excessively tired and slow at the end of the shift. The computer will still be going full-speed, waiting for the reels to be mounted.

After the reels are mounted, the operator will thread the tape thru the drive and feed the tape onto the file reel. He will again manually release the reel brake. Then he will feed a few feet onto the machine reel and close the drive door. A *load* button or *seek beginning of tape* button is used to cause the drive to go to the beginning of tape reflective spot. No light is needed, since the drive will immediately respond to this button. The tape movement is the feedback to the operator. After the drive is at load point, it is put in *ready* or *on-line* status. Since this does not necessarily result in any immediate movement of the drive, a light is necessary to tell the operator that he did push the button far enough. Remember, the operator may be replacing twenty reels per hour, and after the seventh hour, he may not be too energetic in pushing every button.

Certain other lights are also needed for good system operation. Most of the time it is the console operator who will use these other lights.

A *file protect* or *write enable* light is needed. This light is on when the file reel is mounted on the drive without a plastic ring. The removal of the plastic ring means that no writing is to be done on that reel. This type of protection is given to master tapes, program tapes, and history tapes. The light is a positive feedback to the operator that the drive has recognized the special status of this reel. An operator will be quick to investigate if this light doesn't come on when he thinks it should.

A *select, operate,* or *working* light is needed. This light tells the operator that the computer is working directly with this drive. Normally the light will flash on and off. Or it may glow dimly because the commands are coming too fast for the light to follow. In any case, operators soon learn to recognize the rhythm of the *select* lights. When a program is working correctly, the regularity of the lights or the intensity of the light will provide the operator with the confidence to go get a cup of coffee. The lack of the expected indication will hold the operator's attention until conditions are normal.

In these days of variable recording density, a density light is needed. If a CPU is processing tapes of different densities, the control units have to be told at what density to work. If the program and operator aren't together on what density the reel is, repeated read errors will result. Most computer sites have their reels marked as to their densities. A light on the drive is easily checked against the marking on the reel to determine that they are in agreement. In some machines it may be convenient to have a density switch, so that the operator can change the reading density. Of course the switch does not affect the density on tape already written.

Any good tape drive system will be able to sense some internal problems, such as a blown fuse, an open circuit breaker, a door interlock that is not closed, or too high an internal temperature. These and some other problems can be detected by the drive circuits. When one of these conditions occurs, the drive cannot be put on line. An operator can easily waste a minute pushing the *ready* button trying to get the drive to go on line. A simple interlock light would immediately tell him that he left a door open, the solution being to investigate, or to call a service man. An interlock or fuse light is valuable feedback. Finally, every drive should have an *indicator* light. This light is turned on by the computer. It is turned on to call attention to a particular drive. For example, after a computing job is finished, the CPU will rewind the tape. It will then type out on the typewriter, "REMOVE REELS FROM DRIVE 1 LABEL 1 2 3 4 5 REMOVE REELS FROM DRIVE 2 LABEL 2 3 4 5 6" and so on. But the time is 2:00 a.m., and the operators don't see too well or remember much at this time of day. Therefore, after the CPU has typed out the instructions, it will turn a *remember* light on the drive. The operator will go to the drive, with the light on, and remove the reel. The light will be turned off automatically as the drive goes off line. Since the CPU is still awake, it will be able to check that a manual operation took place when the *indicator* light goes off.

Threading, loading, and unloading a drive are taking place in the shadow of the doors and cabinets. Room lighting generally does not penetrate the inner working of the drive. Therefore, auxiliary lighting should be mounted on the drive as working light. This may not be needed on all drives. However, if the drive mechanism is shielded from room lights, a working light is needed.

From this discussion it can be seen that lights on a tape drive are functional. They are also pretty, and make an impressive display in a computer room, especially with all other lights out. The chief function of drive lights is to provide a rapid feedback to the operators. This rapid feedback speeds up the correction process and saves money.

## light reliability

In order for the operators to respond rapidly to the lights, they must have confidence in them. This means that rapid burn-out or marginal lights have no place in a computer tape drive. Lights are sensitive to vibration and over-voltage. Reliability in lights on a tape drive is more than just hanging light bulbs on a drive door. The light bulbs should be low voltage so that the filaments are larger and better able to stand mechanical shock. The light bulbs should be run below rated voltage so that they last and last and last. Finally, when they do burn out, replacement should be so simple that an operator can do it at 3:00 o'clock on a Sunday morning.

## tape drive designation

As indicated previously, a selector or indicator switch will make a running of a computer program simpler. A program will be written with tape transports 1, 2, 3, and 4 in mind. Which particular drive is number 1 is of no concern to the programmer. However, day-to-day service problems may cause the number of a drive to be changed. Suppose that drives A, B, C, D, and E have been numbered 1, 2, 3, 4, and 5 respectively. Because the program is written for 1, 2, 3, 4, each day drives A, B, C, D are used on this program. Drive E is not used. One day drive C develops trouble. Drive C cannot be used. A simple change of the selector switches makes the following change. Drives A, B, C, D and E are numbered 1, 2, not used, 3, and 4. When the program is run, it will never know that drives 3 and 4 are different than previously. Since most drives are identical the numbering system can be shifted about without affecting the program. These changes can be made without change to the program.

There are other reasons for shifting the numbering system of drives. If a program is updating files, the processor may read most of the files in the library. The library can contain several hundred reels of tape. The operator must move several hundred reels of tape from the library to the drives. Also, he must mount, demount, and move the reels back to the library. A small traffic problem can develop right in the computer room.

The program will generally be written so that all the tapes are read on one of two drives in "flip-flop." This means that the CPU will read from one drive while a second drive is loaded or unloaded. The CPU will flip over to the newly loaded drive and allow the old one to be unloaded. The CPU will work back and forth like this through the several hundred reels of tape. The operators may change the numbering of the drives so that the CPU will flip-flop two drives that are near the library. This sort of numbering change does not affect the program, but it makes the traffic problem much simpler.

Note that this numbering change could be made by modifying the program. But the possibility of error is so great, and the possible results can be so disastrous, that changing the numbering system on the drive is better. If the program is modified, a wrong bit may be placed in memory. This wrong bit may never be seen until the CPU updates a hundred reels wrong. However, in changing the drive numbers, no such problem can occur. Only the drive numbers can be changed; no other part of the program can be affected. The *select* light is positive feedback that the change was right or wrong.

Many computer rooms have some tape drives located forty or fifty feet from the console. The operator at the console must also know what the drive designations are. He wants to check which drives are going to be flip-flopped. And he wants to check the program to determine that the designated drives are giving the customary responses. From having previously run the program, the operator will know that drive 2 will start and stop over long bursts of records. However, drive 3 will buzz along over each individual record. This simple audio and visual feedback tells the operator to push the *stop* button, or lean back and relax. Fast feedback corrects errors faster and saves money.

### emergency unload

Once in a while a piece of dirt will become lodged in the tape oxide. This dirt will cause read errors. The only way to remove the dirt is to unload the drive, then carefully scrape or wash the dirt off the tape. This scraping is usually performed with all the interest and speculation that one expects in human surgery. Both events are taken seriously for similar reasons. The scraping may prove disastrous. However, at 3:00 a.m. on the day before the payroll is due emergency measures are justified. When this sort of thing must be done, unload switches are necessary to open up the drive. Automatic unload after a rewind is the normal case. For the exceptional case, manual unloads are necessary.

### controls for off-line

Digital tape drives are connected to other devices besides computers. For example, off-computer printing is done. Off-computer operations are also referred to in the trade as *off-line*. *On-line* means working with the computer. Off-line printing, off-line card punching, and off-line card-to-tape conversion is frequently done. When off-line equipment is used, there are certain other control functions which are needed.

An off-line device may be printing out billing statements. The device is reading from a tape drive and printing on prepared forms. The operator's attention is attracted because the printing stopped. One of the forms becomes jammed and several statements are overprinted on one line. The operator straightens the forms and backspaces the tape. On off-line application, tape movement controls are needed besides the ones already described.

Tape drives present problems in off-line operation. The operator cannot read the magnetic tape. All his manipulation of the tape must be by inference from the results. The operator should be provided with any aids possible to insure manual tape manipulation.

In the forms jammed example, the operator will want to backspace the tape after the paper is straightened out. He may backspace the tape several records and then see what record is printed out. If the record printed out on the test is one that has been printed out before, he can figure how many more backspaces or forward spaces he needs.

In this example, the test line printed out account number 578. Since the last complete form printed out was 574, the operator knows that he must backspace three more statements. Three statements include: three header records, three body records, and three trailer records. Nine backspaces will do it. At this point the operator needs help.

Have you ever tried to push a button nine times, and was sure you got nine and not eight or ten? Each backspace button should be effective only on the release. This will insure that switch joggling or poor contact will not cause one push to result in two electronic pulses. Also, each backspace button should activate a counter which indicates how many pushes were registered. This amount of concern for the simple pushing of a button may seem unnecessary. For many operators, these details will not be necessary. But all operators aren't that good, and even good operators have bad days. The meter on an off-line printer may run at $60 per hour, or about 1.5 cents per second. In the life time of an off-line printer, it doesn't take many paper jams per week to pay for the niceties.

Of course similar arguments can be made for the forward space button. But, since most problems involve backspacing, rather than forward spacing, counters and indicators on the forward space do not have the same return on investment.

## manual operations

Loading a drive is the lowest operation on a CPU (see Chapter 9 for trends; see Chapter 8 for discussion of reel hubs). It is important that all possible attention be given to making loading as convenient as possible. When examining a drive for "loadability" look for these points. Can a drive be opened up with one hand? Frequently an operator will be carrying a reel of tape in one hand. Can he open and close the door, push any buttons, and unlatch any catches with one hand?

The first thing an operator will do after the drive is opened is to mount the reel. Most reel hubs use an expansion rubber ring to grip the reel. The reel hub requires three or four turns of a knob before the rubber is compressed enough to grip the reel firmly. It would be well to check with other users to determine if this drive has trouble with the reel hub. Check with the operators; they will know. Don't ask the Vice President, because he will have no idea.

A drive that uses a rubber expansion ring can have several problems that can cost seconds every time it is loaded. The rubber can stick to the previous reel. When the rubber sticks to the reel, the reel is hard to take off. Operators then pull on the reel and damage the tape. On the other hand, the rubber may not expand enough to grip the reel firmly. In this case, the reel comes off easy enough—too easily. Reels that are not gripped tightly may come off the hub during operation and wander around the inside of the covers, spilling tape in strange places. This can be dangerous to the data and personnel. A loaded reel which spins out of a drive can hurt anyone it strikes. These two problems are the most common with rubber expansion ring hubs. Less common problems are the knobs breaking off and the parts bending out of shape. These faults are difficult to find out by inspection, and the best source of information is another operator.

After the operator has mounted the reel, he must then thread the tape through the mechanism. The word thread is well used. Some transports are very difficult to thread. It is well to note precisely what must be done with the tape after the reel is mounted. Most drives require that the end of the tape be guided through the mechanism, over the head, and then through more mechanism, and finally onto the take-up reel. Note if there is finger room to guide the tape through all these places. If there is no finger room, what is the alternative?

Some drives can be loaded by taking tape directly from one reel onto the second reel and then threading the tape. Since both ends on the tape are securely fastened by a reel, less finger room is required. Some drives require a leader. I am of the opinion that leaders are the ideal way to thread a drive. However, there is one problem. The industrial standard does not require a leader. The ASA standard tape does not require leader connectors on tape. Therefore anyone who uses leaders uses them alone.

After the drive is mechanically loaded, the operator closes the doors and pushes the buttons to tell the computer that the drive is on line. Oops, slam that door a second time, it didn't catch the first time. Each one of these minor annoyances seems like nothing until you remember that the computer is waiting on this loading. And the computer's meter runs at $100 per hour.

## interlocks

Every drive should be properly interlocked to prevent accidents.

This means that a sleepy operator cannot open doors and reach into the drive works while reels or capstans are still turning. The insurance and moral problems are enough to dictate good interlocks. However, on tape drive there are other considerations that make good interlocks important. We have already seen that the CPU may be waiting on the loading and unloading of this drive. How fast an operator services a drive is related to his confidence in its safety. If there is a lingering doubt that this thing may still be turning while he has his hands in it, each move is slowed with caution. Caution is good. But unnecessary caution costs money.

The users would do well to carefully examine the interlocks on the tape drives. How foolproof are they? How reliable? Can you slam the door 500 times and still have the interlocks work? Is there a doubt about any switch failing? Keep this thought in mind. The design engineer loves to design good tape drives. But he only worked on the interlocks because the sales department insisted on it.

### over-all review

After each detail of a drive is examined for function and reliability, the whole should be seen. Is the drive position at the right height so that an average operator can load the drive? Is the drive so low a stool should be provided? Is it so high that a ladder should be considered? Where are the buttons and indicators? Can they be reached easily? Will the indicators show across the room? Can an operator at the console recognize the various indicators by their size or color? Does the tape system present a pleasing appearance? Since the tape drives are the only mechanical moving objects in a computer, your visitors will spend most of the time looking at the reels go around.

Examine the skins on the tape drives. How do they come off? What provisions must be made for maintenance? Is service accomplished from the front, sides, or back, or all three? What provisions must be made for storing the skins? If tape drives are located where covers cannot be stored, the skins will have to be carried through the computer room during maintenance. Does the drive make provision for convenient outlets for service personnel? If not, plan for extension cords trailing through the computer room.

### in summary

Tape drives are the primary source and output for computer data. Since computers eat information very fast, tape drives are very busy. The tape drives are our means of communicating to the computer. Since tape drives face both the computer and us, let's be sure the human factors have not been overlooked. The computer will insure the machine factors have not been overlooked. But people will frequently adapt to slow and inefficient procedures. Careful analysis is necessary to assure that all human functions are necessary and fast.

## CHAPTER 7. Questions

1. What is the general function of lights and switches on a tape drive?
2. Justify the following lights: On Line, Write Enable, and Select.
3. What manual movement of tape is likely on an off line printer or punch?
4. What manual operations are needed on a drive working with a computer?

# 8 allied areas

IN ORDER TO GET MAXIMUM EFFICIENCY out of a tape system, we must be concerned about certain allied areas. These areas are not necessarily a physical part of the tape drive. For example, we should be concerned with:

1. *What does the advertised 'KC' transfer rate mean?*
2. *What is the industrial standard coding (IBM and ASA)?*
3. *How can the programs be changed to improve tape efficiency?*
4. *How close should tabs be kept on maintenance people?*
5. *How can the tape system efficiency be measured?*
6. *What is the life of the tape media?*
7. *What protection should be made against a major disaster?*

These concerns are not part of the mechanics of the tape system. However, poor management in these areas can make the best mechanical system turn out poor results. Proper concern will cause mediocre mechanics to turn out acceptable results. The following pages will deal with the allied areas in the tape system.

## transfer rates

One of the first questions of any computer user is the transfer rate of a drive. How fast can data be written out, and how fast can it be read into the computer? The tape drive manufacturers make much of the Peak Transfer Rate. The Peak Rate is the maximum speed at which data can come from a drive. But there are other rates which are more important. The Effective Rate is the rate at which data comes off the drive when you consider inter-record gaps. There is also a Day Rate. This is the rate at which data comes off a drive when you average the results over a full working day. This last rate takes into account load-unload time, rewind time, and maintenance. The transfer rate is the first measure of a drive. But which transfer rate is the measure?

The manufacturers quote figures like 15 KC, 62 KC, 90/180 KC. What was that last one, 90/180 KC? It seems to indicate that a drive will operate in more than one mode. These figures are similar to those coming out of a beauty contest. They're interesting, but they are no help when picking a wife.

In order to get down to the problem, start out with Figure 50. This

/ INCH REORDS , 0.75 INCH GAPS

**Fig. 50**—DEVELOPED MAGNETIC TAPE. This is a diagram of magnetic tape to show its appearance when developed. Developing is accomplished by causing small iron particles to come near enough to the oxide that they are attracted to the magnetic pole tips that are laid down during writing.

is the layout of a piece of magnetic tape that has been developed. Developing a piece of magnetic tape allows us to see the magnetized areas of the tape. We can see where data is and where it is not. When the tape drive is reading in the data area it is transmitting data to the computer at its Peak Rate. This is the fastest that the drive can put out data, for the given density. This Peak Rate is the number that is quoted by the manufacturer. From the diagram you can see that the Peak Rate only applies to the data area. And the data area is half the amount of tape. This simple fact is very important.

The Character Rate of information coming off a drive is a product of three things: the density of the information, the speed of the tape past the head, and the number of tracks read in parallel. This last point is generally overlooked because 95 percent of all tape is 7-track tape. (One channel has no information, as it is normally parity, or checking track.) But this is due to change. The new ASA standard is 9-track tape. One of the ASA tracks is not defined. Some companies will use seven data tracks and some will use eight data tracks. Now the KC rate as defined by most manufacturers will be more difficult to understand. Most companies pay little attention to the number of data tracks.

This tendency is very strong. One company had eight information channels rather than the normal six. This same company advertised their tape as 110 KC (meaning 110 KC, eight-bit characters). However, since KC rate is so tied to the six-bit character, their ads could have honestly said 146 KC six-bit characters. It is unfortunate that the industrial KC rate is based on six bits per character. In order to keep from comparing apples and oranges, we should talk about kilo-bit rate, KB, instead of kilo-character, KC.

If we don't watch our terms very carefully we may become confused. Most manufacturers will continue to advertise KC rates based on a six-bit character. Many times manufacturers will slip in figures like 90/180 KC. This figure will come into being because of the numeric pack. In the ASA code for magnetic tape, seven data bits are needed to define or specify the characters. However, a numeric can be specified with four bits. By taking advantage of the undefined track, eight data tracks are available. Two numeric characters can be written in the place of one ASA character. The numerics have thus been packed two to one. Of course if your data is predominately numbers, the numeric pack gives you twice the transfer rate. This is how a manufacturer will justify the use of 90/180 KC.

## kilo-bit rate

Please note however, that if you figure the bit content of the data, the ratio is not so good. The 80 KC of seven-bit data characters gives 560 KB rate (kilo-bit), 160 KC numeric pack mode of four bits per numeric gives 640 KB. The numeric pack has a higher bit transfer rate in the ratio of 8 to 7, not 2 to 1. If our computer is not able to take advantage of seven channels of information, the numeric pack may well give us a 2 to 1 increase in rate. However, a binary computer will only see an advantage of 8 to 7 for the numeric pack mode.

In order to reduce the fog content of the remaining discussion, I will always include two figures whenever KC rate is written. A KC rate in six-bit characters will be listed. This can be used to compare with the advertisement. Then, I simply list a KB rate which is the bit rate of the drive. The bit rate takes into account all factors affecting the peak transfer rate of a drive. The KB rate can be used to compare various drives, no matter what their configurations.

## peak transfer rate

The Peak Rate of a drive is defined as the data rate occurring as the read heads pass over the recorded portion of the tape (see Fig. 50 again). The Peak Rate really doesn't help very much when you are trying to figure program times. You also want to know how much time you are going to spend in the gaps. The gaps produce "zero" transfer rate. The operating speed of a program may be limited primarily by input-output rates. Thus, the time the tape drive spends reading the gaps is as important as the time spent reading data. This leads to a term which I define as Effective Rate.

### effective rate

The Effective Rate is the data rate that we will see when our records are written on the drive of our choice. So Effective Rate can be altered by writing longer records. Longer records make the gaps a smaller proportion of the total. Then the Effective Rate will approach the

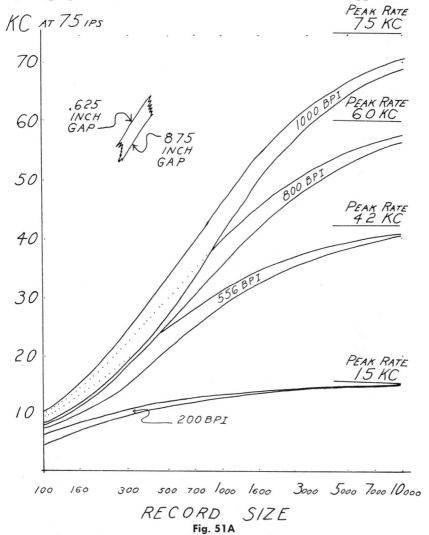

**Fig. 51A**

**Fig. 51**—EFFECTIVE TRANSFER RATES/RECORD SIZE. These diagrams show how the block length and gap size affects the transfer rates of a drive. The top of the curve is the transfer rate for a gap of .625 inches, the bottom of the curve is for a gap of .875 inches. The KC rate quoted is the frame rate. Multiply this rate by the number of tracks being read to obtain the bit rate.

Peak Rate. But don't be surprised if the Effective Rate is still lower than the Peak Rate. Figures 51 and 52 give the Effective Rates for various size gaps and records.

Notice how the Effective Rate drops off with short records. When a computer is writing a magnetic tape which is used to bill a customer, the record size may be 60 characters long. The difference between 75 KC and 15 KC peak frame rate is not so apparent for records of this length. Similar comparisons could be made for tapes coming from card readers, or tapes used to punch cards.

Effective Rate is a function of the Peak Rate, the size of the records, and the size of the gap. When writing tapes for bills, or a punch, or when reading a tape resulting from a card conversation, nothing can be done about the record length. The record size is fixed by the paper document. However, something can be done about the record gap size.

### how to measure inter-record gaps

Most inter-record gaps are described as ¾ inch, with a tolerance of

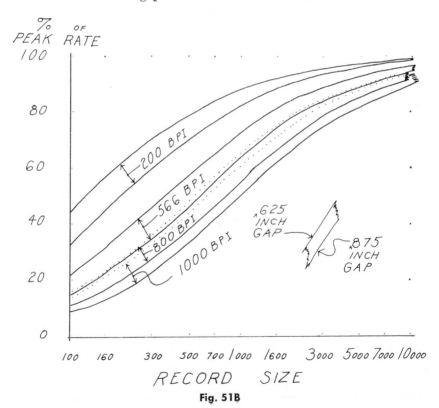

Fig. 51B

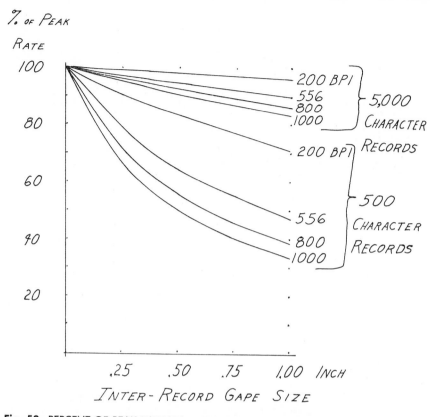

**Fig. 52—PERCENT OF PEAK RATE/GAP SIZE.** This chart shows the effect of reducing the gap a size on two sizes of records, 500, and 5,000. Gap size has much more effect on small record lengths than it has on larger records.

plus $\frac{1}{16}$ and minus $\frac{1}{8}$. The figures imply that the nominal is $\frac{3}{4}$ of an inch. However, that may not be true. It was pointed out in Chapter 4 that the size of the inter-record gap is a function of the speed of the capstan system, the delay timers, and the accuracy of the adjustment. Also the plus tolerance is meaningless as skip or erase gaps may be 3.5 inches long. Just how well our particular system is doing is open to question. And before any changes are suggested, it is a good idea to have the facts.

We can measure the size of the gaps on tape. This can be done by developing several hundred feet of tape, then a ruler will tell us the size of the gaps. Besides being dangerous to the tape this does not give a very good statistical sample. The best way to measure tape record gaps is with the computer. Have a program written which will measure all the gaps, and print out the average and the extremes.

In order for a computer to be able to measure the length of the inter-record gap, it must have some basic characteristics. The computer must be able to tell when the first character comes in off tape. Second, the computer must be able to tell when the last character comes in off the tape record. This latter point is often obtained by implication. As soon as the tape is not busy, the drive is not reading anything. Finally the computer must be able to calculate while tape is being read. Many of these characteristics are available in computers under little suspected commands.

In measuring the gaps between records, we are not interested in reading data, we are just interested in when the tape drive is finished

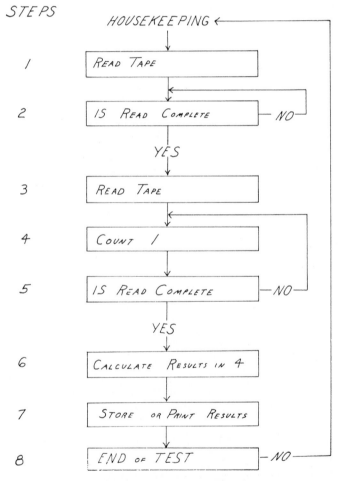

**Fig. 53**—FLOW DIAGRAM FOR GAP MEASURING PROGRAM. This shows the generalized flow of a program which is measuring the size of the inter-record gaps on tape. Computer time is the measuring base.

reading it. Once we have determined that we have a computer which can compute while the tape system is reading a record, and the computer can tell when reading begins and ends, we are ready to write a gap measuring program.

See Figure 53 for a flow diagram of program. After technical housekeeping is done, Step 1 starts the tape moving. It is important that the computer keep the drive moving the tape through the inter-record gap. This program uses time to measure the gaps. Time can only be used to figure the inter-record gap if tape does not stop in the gap. Therefore, this program is designed to move tape through the gap at full speed and determine how much time it took.

Step 1 starts the tape. Step 2 determines when the last character has been read by the drive. At this point the read head is entering the inter-record gap at full speed. Step 3 issues a read command in order to keep the tape moving at full speed and so the computer will be able to tell when the first character of the next record has been read.

In your particular computer, this may be a read command or some other command. Steps 4 and 5 create a small loop which is counting the time for the first character to come into the computer. While the computer is revolving in Steps 4 and 5, the drive is passing through the inter-record gap at full speed. When the first character of the record is sensed, the computer breaks out of the counting loop. An inter-record gap has been measured by counting the passing of time and knowing the tape speed.

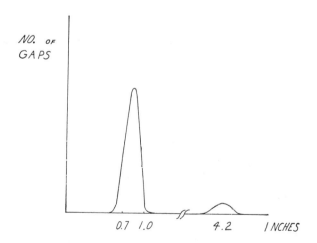

**Fig. 54**—STATISTICAL DISTRIBUTION OF GAP SIZES. These curves show the number of records with each size gap. The increase in number of gaps at 4.2 is due to the use of the skip command. The skip command jumps over bad tape by generating a 3.5 inch gap. This, plus the normal start-up gap, gives 4.2 inch gaps after a skip command.

In Step 6, the total count of Steps 4 and 5 is multiplied by the time it took to go around the loop. This will give the time that the drive spent reading the inter-record gap. Next the speed of the drive is multiplied by this time. For example, 75 inch-per-second tape speed is multiplied by 1,098 microseconds to give 0.821 inches. This is the size of the inter-record gap. In Step 8 the above operation is repeated for the entire tape. The results from each calculation are stored. This particular program measures every other inter-record gap on tape. For our purpose this is enough.

After many gaps are measured, the average, high, and low should be calculated. Also a statistical distribution should be made (see Fig. 54). This data tells us that this tape was written with an average inter-record gap of 0.85 or 0.1 inch over the implied nominal. The change in the distribution curve at 4.0 inches is due to erase command. Each time the program finds that it cannot write on a piece of tape, it will skip over 3.5 inches of tape and try again. Therefore, there are a number of gaps which are four inches long.

## cost of large gaps

Now let us do some simple figuring to determine how much it will cost to have an extra 0.1 inch in the gap. Let us assume:

1. We are writing 100 character records to be printed.
2. The computer cost is $100 per hour.
3. The program speed is tape limited (I/0 Bound).
4. That it takes an hour to write all the print-out tapes.

These are all reasonable assumptions. In an hour, the computer could read-write between 9 and 15 reels of tape. The exact number is not important in our calculations.

At 500 characters per inch (500 bpi) a 100 character record takes 0.2 inches. An inter-record gap of 0.85 would make the distance from the beginning of one record to the beginning of the next record 1.05 inches rather than 0.95 inches. The inter-record gap is 0.1 inches over the nominal. If the nominal could be obtained, the 60-minute program would be reduced by 0.1/1.05 inches per record or 9.5%. The cost of the computer for this job could be reduced from $100 to $90 for a saving of $10 per hour.

## to summarize

For programs which are writing short records, such as are used in printing or punching, 0.1 inch increase in the inter-record gap may increase your computer cost 10%.

## what can be done

Some people have alraady run gap-measuring programs. These programs indicate that a 0.1 inch increase in gap size is not unusual.

What can be done? Maybe nothing. However, let's spend a moment and analyze what causes record gaps to be too large. First the design of the transport may be such that the drive cannot write smaller gaps (see Chapter 4 for the reasons). If this is the case, talk to the salesman who sold the system. Let's look at the variables which can be controlled. For one thing, the drive can be out of adjustment. This can be recognized if one drive generates longer gaps on the same program than another drive. If this is the case, let your service personnel know your problem. The size of the inter-record gaps are frequently controlled by a timer in the tape control unit. The timer may be out of adjustment, or even deliberately set long. Service personnel will sometimes set these timers long so that they do not have to keep the drive mechanisms up to the mark. Check to see if these timers can be reduced. Finally, the rhythm of your particular program may be causing the inter-record gaps to be long.

This last statement needs some explanation. The tape drive stop-and-go mechanism requires some mechanical movement. In a pinch roller drive, the roller itself must be moved. In an air capstan, both the air in various chambers and the valve must be moved. It is a law of nature that whenever you start or stop a mass, the mass will give or spring. This mass and spring gives a natural period of oscillation. Strike a desk, and you hear one sound; kick a door and you hear another sound. Each one of these sounds is caused by the object oscillating in response to your fist or foot. It is also true with a tape drive. When a pinch roller slams into the capstan, or the air rushes through a valve, there is a natural period of oscillation.

If your computer program happens to give stop-and-go commands in rhythm with the natural frequency of the tape drive stop-and-go mechanism, we can cause variation in record gaps. Most drives have been tested for this, and the amount of variance is well within the allowed tolerance. However, the variation may not be. This is another reason for the service personnel setting the tap timers long. See Figure 55 on page 110 for inter-record gap variation.

The term *go-down time* means the time between a stop command and the time to the next *go* command. This time is the time that the go line to the drive is saying stop. When viewed on an oscilloscope, this is the time the go line is down, go-down time. The chart shows that at zero go-down time, a perfect inter-record gap is generated. However, as go-down time increases, so does the size of the gap. The reason for this is that the tape coasts for 0.5 to 1.0 MS at full speed. However, the timer starts to time for the size of the inter-record gap when the go line comes up. Therefore, if the *go* command is given 1 MS after the *stop* command, the go-down time is 1 MS. The drive coasted through the inter-record gap for one 1MS at full speed.

The record gap timer pays no attention to coast, and times out from the *start* command. The gap is made 1 MS larger because of the coast. 1

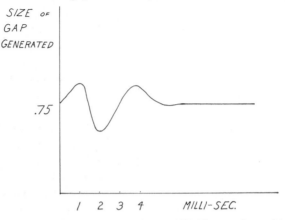

**Fig. 55**—GAP SIZE AS FUNCTION OF GO DOWN TIME. The gap that a drive will produce is a function of the time that the drive is told to stop. If the drive is never told to stop, the timing base changes and mechanical resonances cause the gap to vary. Each type of drive has its own peculiar curve.

MS can be 0.07 inches to 0.15 inches, depending on the speed of the drive. The graph shows another record gap increase at 3.0 MS. This is due to the *start* command being aided by natural oscillation of the start mechanism. The natural vibration of the mechanism will tend to cause a restart. (In a good drive it will not cause any additional motion, but it will tend to cause it.) If, at that moment of tendency, a *start* command is issued, the drive will start very quickly. Since the timer doesn't know this, it times out normal. The drive started very fast, and like a distance runner, it went farther because it started faster. The inter-record gap is longer.

The valley is in the curve at 2 MS and has just the opposite effect from the situation described above. If the start command is given when the natural vibration is to stop, the start is very slow. This will produce a short inter-record gap. Slow starters don't run as far in the same time as fast starters.

### altering the program

What can the programmer do about this? It depends. It depends on the program, the drive, and how much time is spent in this mode of operation. First of all, one has to determine that he has a problem. If the gap-measuring program indicates that the gaps produced are well within tolerance, there is nothing to be done. However, I suspect that at least some of our programs are producing some long gaps, or some short ones. Short gaps lead to read errors. If the programs that produce long gaps are insignificant in computer time, don't bother to do anything. If the computer time is significant, you have a problem.

First of all, get with the service personnel, and be sure that the drives are up to the mark. Some drives have an adjustment for coasting time, and for the amount of start power. If the starting power is very strong, it can overcome any natural vibration tendencies which cause long gaps. If you determine that the drives are OK, and you are involved in programming rhythm causing a record gap variation problem, don't give up. Many computers have overlap as a standard feature. If this is so, the timing of the issuance of the *write* command can be varied. A program is normally written to do all computation, and then write out a record. Get with the program and see if the *write* command can't be given half-way through the computation. Maybe the *write* command can be issued before the computation is even started. In some programs, this may mean that occasionally the drive is up to speed and running, and the computations are not completed. In this case, provisions must be made to write a dummy record, backspace, and re-write. The idea of changing the timing of the write command will meet with some opposition. No one likes to make a program illogical in timing to accommodate a drive. Tape drives are like people, they may give you fits, but you can't do without them. Do the best you can.

## gapless tape

After all this, you may still find that you are spending considerable time writing inter-record gaps. Maybe you should consider gapless tape. Gapless tape is one which has the inter-record gaps reduced to 0.1 inches or less. The records are written so close together that for all practical purposes there is no gap. Before jumping into this one, stop. There are problems with gapless tape. If there weren't problems, all tape would be gapless. A tape drive can not stop in the proper gap. Consequently, if the computer ever lets the drive stop, the tape must be backspaced until data is found. Then the tape is started, and the first data ignored until the small gap is found. We can see that gapless tape is fine until we stop. Then the reason for a long gap is pretty obvious. Backspacing is slow. However, if the computer spends a good deal of time writing short records, gapless tape should be considered. Circuits can be designed in off-line equipment that will handle gapless tape. The question is, is the computer cost reduced enough to justify the circuit expense associated with gapless tape?

Considerable time has been spent on the inter-record gap problem. The reason is that gaps cost money. If the size records are fixed by the output media, the only thing left to work with is the physical gap. However, there are other ways to improve the Effective transfer rate of a drive. Remember, the Effective transfer rate is Peak transfer rate modified by the gaps. But the graphs 51 and 52 also show that the size record plays a part. Effective rate is lowest for the shortest records. For very long records, the Effective rate approaches the Peak transfer rate. So another way to reduce the effects of inter-record gaps is to use larger records. At this point, I can hear the programmers scream.

## record blocking

Blocking records is a normal computer practice. But of course, blocking records required more memory space (because this means that several logical records are read in at one time). And next to good programmers, memory space is the hardest item to come by. Nevertheless, blocking tape increases efficiency. If the computer is input or output limited, the Effective rate has to be made to approach the Peak rate. Figure 51 shows how this can be done for various size records. Anyone who is operating on an average of below 60 should review his operation. Everything may be OK. But the chances are that there are a good many things that could be done to materially improve the Effective rate of data transfer into and out of the tape transports.

Note also that on short records the effects of recording density are very small. The reason for this is that the inter-record gap is such a large percentage that reducing the recording length from 10 percent to 5 percent isn't important. The gaps are from 90 percent to 95 percent. In general the most important change which can be made in most systems is to increase the average size of the records. This may require that the programs be written differently. Parts of the programs may have to be kept on a storage drum, disk, or tape. When this part of the program is needed, it will be called in from storage.

In some computer rooms where the average program run is six to twelve minutes, this involves an entire change in philosophy. But then, that is the path of progress.

## short gaps on tape

There is one final note about how one goes about improving the

Effective transfer rate. One company offered a means of generating short gaps on tape. This system took a little longer to write tape in some cases. But it saved each time the record was read.

To start off, most tape transports can reliably read from a shorter gap than they can write. The reason for this is that the read head is 0.3 to 0.25 inches behind the write head. Whenever the write head is up to speed for writing, the read head is up to speed for reading. But the read head is 0.3 inches back of the gap! In other words the read head is ready to work when it has traversed only 60 percent of the gap. One company took advantage of this to write gaps which were only 60 percent as long.

And this is how they did it. The tape gap timers were set to produce gaps 60 percent as long as were needed. If the computer was able to keep the tape moving—that is, the computer always had data available for the next record—tape did not have to stop and go and there was nc problem. If the computer was not able to keep up, and had to let the tape stop, a different sequence took place. The tap stopped normally, then automatically went into a short backspace operation. This short backspace was just enough so that the read head began to read the previous record. This short backspace reduced the size of the gap to a very precise 60 percent. When the next *write* command came along, the tape started to move from a point which was closer to the last record. Not only that, the point of origin was very closely controlled so that the inter-record gap did not vary. If a computer was able to keep up with the tapes, this system made writing a faster action because only 60 percent gaps had to be generated. If the computer could not keep up with the tapes, and had to let a tape stop while another tape was selected, the system made writing slower because the drive had to backspace.

It should be evident that the system may not be practical, if a drive requires a forward-to-backward reverse delay like the 20 MS. But many drives can reverse in 2 to 3 MS. In this 60 percent gap size system, reading was always faster. Writing was sometimes faster and sometimes slower. See Figure 52 for the effects this system would have on Effective transfer rate. One short-sort program ran 40 percent faster with this system.

### start time

We have been discussing the effects that the gap has on the Effective transfer rate. There is one additional small area of concern associated with interrupted gaps—the start-stop time of a drive. It is closely tied to the gap size. Any drive must start and stop. It is possible that one drive would generate small gaps, but have a very slow start time. In a start-stop mode the program is interested in time, not size of gap.

A slow start time is possible if the drive takes a long time before any media movement begins. Once media begins to move acceleration is very rapid. This type of operation is not likely, but it is possible—watch out for it. A tape drive manufacturer may have a time restriction on just how fast you can start and stop. This restriction can appear as a long start time in a record gap. This costs money.

Drive # 4   75 ips

| ENTRY NO. | LOAD/UNLOAD TIME | REWIND TIME | COMPUTER TIME | LENGTH OF TAPE USED | UTILIZATION RATIO | DATA TIME | DRIVE IDLE TIME | TAPE SYSTEM IDLE TIME | MAINTENANCE TIME | ELAPSED TIME | COMMENTS |
|---|---|---|---|---|---|---|---|---|---|---|---|
| | 1 | 2 | 3 | 4 | 5 | 6 | 7 | 8 | 9 | 10 | |
| 1 | .7 | | | | | | | | | 9 00 | Reel Stuck |
| 2 | | .5 | 200 | | 60% | .3 | | | | 9.10 | Sort # 34/ |
| 3 | | 1.5 | | 1500 | 60% | 2.4 | | | | 925 | |
| 4 | .3 | | 25 | | | | | | | 925 | |
| 5 | | | | | | | | | 2 | 921 | Light bulb |
| 6 | | | | | | | 7 | | | 934 | |
| 7 | .2 | | | | | | | | | 934 | Input cards |
| 8 | | 2.0 | 6 | 2000 | 20% | 1.0 | | | | 940 | for job #32 |
| 9 | | | | | | | | 2 | | 942 | Set up #98 |
| 10 | | | | | | | | | | | |
| | 1.2 | 4.0 | 31 | 3700 | — | 3.7 | 9 | | 2 | 42 | |

$$\frac{Data\ Time}{Total\ Time} \times Peak = \frac{3.7}{42} \times 60KC = \boxed{5.3\ KC}$$
Day Rate

**Fig. 56—CLIP BOARD CHART.** This is the filled out form that one can use to determine the day rate of a drive. The text gives the explanation of each column.

## day transfer rate

So far we have seen that Peak transfer rates of a drive are reduced by the inter-record gaps. This lower rate is due to the time lost starting and stopping in the gaps, or just passing over the inter-record gaps. But Effective rate is still not the whole story. What we really want to know is, "How fast does that thing work, day in, day out?" This takes into account the load-unload time, rewind time, maintenance time, and any other nonproductive times. The Day rate describes the drive as we see it, all day long.

In order to obtain the Day rate, we have to sit in the computer room with a clipboard and stopwatch. The times we would measure can be combined with Effective rate to give us Day rate. This Day rate will tell us what the drive's transfer rate is, averaged over a full working day. Some of the factors that go to making up a Day rate are:

*1. *Load-Unload*
*2. *Rewind Time*
*3. *Computer Time*
*4. *Length of Tape Used (Tape passing time)*
5. *Utilization Ratio (obtain from Effective rate)*
6. *Data Time (the time the drive is transferring data to the computer)*
*7. *Drive Idle Time*
8. *System Idle Time (tape system)*
*9. *Maintenance Time*
*10. *Elapsed Time (clock time)*

Numbers 1, 2, 3, 4, 7, 9, and 10 (the ones with asterisks) are measured by the man with the clipboard and stopwatch. The others are calculated. In the Appendix is a detailed description of the procedure for determining these times. Here we will assume we have the results, and will determine what can be done.

## results

Figure 56 shows a chart filled in with all the numbers. Let's review the numbers and see what they mean.

## load-unload time

A one-minute figure is high for load-unload time. A normal drive should be able to be unloaded in 20 to 30 seconds. If your time is much over 30 seconds look for trouble. Do the doors all work well? Are the door catches a constant annoyance to the operators? They may be costing you money. Notice the time it takes to mount and demount the reel. This is the time that operator takes to push a reel onto a hub and tighten it up. Does the reel come off the hub freely, or must he pull the reel off? Pulling reels off hubs is slow, and damages tape.

If your operators are spending excess time mounting and demounting, get with the service people and the manufacturers to find out what can be done. The rubber in the hub may be the wrong material, or too old. The parts in the hub may be bent or worn. Each of these problems will cause the hub to fail to grip the reel, or to release when it should. (Can't the manufacturer supply you with fast demount reel hubs)?

The ideal reel lock hub would require no more than a half-twist to tighten a reel on the hub. A push button or an easy reverse twist would release the reel. This type of hub would save 10 seconds on every mount and demount cycle. And remember, this is computer time at $.03 per second.

### rewind time

This is the time that the drive spends rewinding tape. It is strictly a function of the drive, and cannot be changed except by a mechanical change to the drive. However, one shouldn't thus walk away from this problem. There are some drives that will rewind a reel of tape in less than one minute, and there are others which will take as long as four minutes to rewind a reel of tape. The basic design is sometimes a limiting factor on how fast rewind can be. If rewind speed is no greater than twice normal reading speed, investigate the possibility of a higher speed rewind. Perhaps the manufacturer can put in a three-to-one capstan motor if capstan rewind is being used. If reel-to-reel rewind is being used, a high voltage on the motors during rewind might pay off. If the computer is waiting during the rewind process, rewind can be expensive, and some extra cost and effort is justified to reduce the time.

### computer time

This time cuts off consideration of the operators, and directs our attention to the program. It gives us a check figure against which we can compare all other computer times. This is the time that the drive is responsive to program commands.

### drive idle time

A certain amount of off-line idle time is unavoidable. However, if this time begins to become a too large a percentage something is wrong.

Do we have too many drives for effective utilization? Maybe our program load and unload routines are poor and we are spending too much time getting ready to use the computer. Perhaps we do not have enough operators. If one man has to do all the setup time for a run, the computer and the drives are going to be idle. It may make good sense to have more operators than can be utilized all the time, so that drives—and hence computer idle time—are kept to a minimum.

## maintenance time

Good maintenance is the key to good drive mechanical operation. However, the drives should not require too much time for this. A number around three percent is reasonable. If the time gets much higher than that, we begin to wonder if new parts wouldn't be better than adjusting old ones. Would more adequate tools and test gear speed up adjustments? The author knows of one case where a certain adjustment required a half-hour every two weeks. A simple jig allowed the adjustment to be made in five minutes. Many times the service personnel are at the tail end of Engineering's thinking. This sort of attitude will show up in this item.

## length of tape used

This is a measurement made on the drive. It is made by marking off the machine's reel of tape in feet, and estimating tape passed before rewind. The figure is used in obtaining all the nonmeasured items in this chart. However, the definite figure has interest all its own. How much tape is being used by the average program? Is so little tape being used per reel that we should consider buying smaller reels of tape and cutting down the inventory? Operators and programmers like to have their own private stock of tape, tape that they know is good. Soon the installation has $80,000 in inventory tape, and the first 10 percent is used. The author knows of one installation that had an average usage of 30 feet, and no reel has had more than 300 feet used. This was a scientific and research installation, but it shows how far the situation can go.

## tape utilization ratio

This number combines with Item 4 to calculate the other items in the list. The utilization ratio is the amount of tape containing data divided by the total tape. The ratio indicates how big the records are in comparison with the gaps. A ratio like $7/10$ would indicate the record to be twice the size of the gaps ($7/10$ data and $3/10$ gaps). If the number is smaller than this, we should find out why records aren't more completely blocked on tape. Why is the system spending so much time passing over blank tape called inter-record gaps? Sometimes more computer memory is the answer. However, I have also seen the case where the program was wasting large areas of memory in read-in read-out buffer areas. A sharp program will require no more than three data areas, a read-in buffer, a read-out buffer and a work area. The data can be rotated between the three, or better yet, the registers can be changed. I have seen programs with five buffer areas for the same work.

### data time and system idle time

Much of a drive's time on line is spent waiting for a command (System Idle Time). Data Time times tell us the time that the drive system is reading or writing as a result of the commands issued by the computer. It is the heart of our investigation.

This time for one drive is not significant. However, the total for all the drives for one program is significant. Data time (total) for all drives should equal twice the Program time, if the computer has simultaneous read and write. This will mean that all during the program, the computer kept one drive writing and one drive reading. If the total time for all the drives does not add up to twice the Program time, the computer is computer limited, not input-output limited. What can be done about making the programs more efficient, and running faster? Perhaps the production jobs should be rewritten in something closer to machine language which will be more efficient. Here is an important line of investigation. This information proves one way or the other that the system is tape-limited or computer-limited.

System Idle time is a check on data time. Idle time and Data time should equal Program time times the number of drives that can be transferring data simultaneously.

### clipboard summary

This chart has been used to indicate where your tape drive time is being used. It is a way of studying your operation to determine what can be done to speed it up. Once we realize what percentage of the drive time is spent with the operators, we can evaluate the human aspects of the drive more carefully. Maintenance time is put in its true perspective. And of course, by comparing the cost per minute of tape drives, we can evaluate the possible saving of spending more or less money on the computer hardware to handle more or fewer tape drives simultaneously. After we have a tape system running, the ratio between

Data time and total of Tape Passing time will tell us how well the programs are packing data on tape. The ratio between Tape Passing time and Computer Idle time will tell us how well the programs are utilizing the facilities of the computer. Don't hesitate to dig out more details.

## program check of drives

The previous discussion has described just how to check out the tape drive times with a stopwatch and a clipboard. This method is simple and sound. However it is manual, and there is something that grates a little about checking on the computer manually. With a little

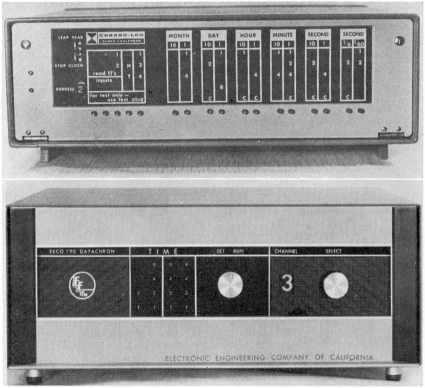

**Fig. 57**—COMPUTER TIME CLOCKS. These are examples of the type of time clocks that are available to put on line with a computer. The computer is then able to read the time directly into memory. These clocks are available in almost any configuration that is required. Courtesy Chrono-Log Corporation and Electronic Engineering Company.

sophistication, you can have the computer check on itself. Not only does this sound better when read from a report, but it is more accurate. Also, it is easier to keep a running chart of how the system is being run every day.

In order to have a computer check on itself, three things are needed. First of all, a computer readable time clock is needed. Figure 57 shows two that will do the job nicely. We will have to have spare memory, like disc files, a drum, or a spare tape transport. And finally, we will have to have the cooperating programmers. Every time the computer issues an instruction to a drive that will require more than one second to complete, the computer will record the time and drive number in the spare memory. When the job is completed, this information is also recorded. This recording takes care of Rewind, Load-Unload times, and Operator times. Next the program can keep a count of; the number of *read* or *write* instructions to a drive, and the number of characters. These numbers will yield Data time, Length of Tape, and Tape Passing time. At the end of every pass, this information is dumped onto the spare memory. At the end of the day a simple program can summarize the information stored by the various programs. Load-Unload time and Drive Idle times cannot be separated by the program. However, this is not important. Load-Unload time can be determined by an occasional manual check. Drive Idle time can be obtained by subtraction. This sort of detailed checking will take some space in the main memory, and it will take a spare permanent memory as indicated before. It can be argued that the history of our industrial improvements is built on management's insistence on accurate measurement of the facts.

## reel identification

If the previous analysis tells us that there is too much Drive Idle time, there are several areas we can investigate. What does an operator have to do once the computer says change reels? Does he have to write an identifying label on the reels? Consider these solutions. Cause the computer to type out reel labels after the rewind begins. The type-out should come as early in the pass as possible. If your installation passes a great deal of tape, typing on gummed stickers may pay for itself in less Idle time. A separate typewriter may be justified.

## reel storage

Can the drives or the tape storage be located so that the operators do not have so far to fetch reels of tape? If both are fixed, are reel teacarts or temporary storage available? Whenever you are looking at the conveniences for an operator, think of the system. It may be cheaper to let a $3-an-hour operator work 100 hours a year or longer, than to provide a $1,500 table, cart, and tape rack. But it is cheaper to provide a $1,500 cart than to keep the $100-per-hour computer waiting 100 hours a year. Strike a balance yourself; you are the one paying for either approach.

## maintenance

Do not be afraid to pay attention to maintenance of the computer. You may be doing your own maintenance or you may be getting maintenance as part of the computer cost.

However it's done, keep track. Keep track of Operator Idle time. This may indicate that door catches are wearing out, that doors don't fit anymore, that buttons and lights are not functioning. It is very easy for maintenance personnel to let the operator convenience items slip, because these items don't show up on the re-run or error reports. Operator inconvenience shows up in longer job times. And of course, these changes may become masked by an increased work load.

## error counts

One item wasn't mentioned in the previous discussion of having the computer check itself—error counts and re-run time. Almost every installation keeps track of the number of errors and re-runs. This is an excellent check on maintenance. When the error count on one drive starts to go up, maintenance is required. Re-run time due to tape drives is most disconcerting. This can be caused by a drive breaking a tape, by writing bad tape, by damaging tape, or by failure of the drive to respond to some commands. All except the last item call for maintenance. If a drive fails to respond to a command and does not give an indication that this happened, watch out. This problem can haunt us for years. For example, suppose that a *write* command is given to a drive. And suppose that the drive does not respond to the command, and does not give an error indication. The computer will have written a record out into thin air. The record which was to be stored on tape is gone, and there is no indication of this. No indication until days, weeks, or years later when we have to read this record back. The record is not on tape, and we have to go back to the source data. This may be impossible. The design of any drive should insure that an error indication is given if the drive fails to respond to a command. Errors for lost commands is one item on which we must be hard-nosed. Insist on this requirement.

## maintenance log

It is a good idea for the maintenance personnel to keep a log for every drive. This log should contain a brief description of all maintenance work and the time.

Do not require that the total time in the log equal the total hours paid to the personnel. This sort of policy leads to a padded log. Also, all parts replacement and mechanical adjustments should be recorded in the log. In fact, certain adjustments and times should be charted. Charting the mechanical or electrical trends in a drive can easily lead to prediction of wearout and failure. This in turn, will lead to replacement just before failure. And replacement just before failure is excellent maintenance.

Incidently, most parts of a tape transport wear out on a basis of on-line time, not chronological time. It would be a great help to maintenance personnel to have a running hour meter connect to record only when a tape is loaded and on-line with the computer. A running hour meter time is a good number to be able to record in a machine log.

## tape wear

For the most part, a reel of magnetic tape cannot be worn out on a digitial tape drive. This was not always the case. However, the introduction of hard binder tape has reduced the wear problem to almost nothing. Tape will last a very long time.

The length of time that tape will last depends on a number of conditions. The author once conducted a tape test to determine wearout time of the tape. The first condition of the test is the shape of the drive. There must be no sharp-edged guides to scratch tape. A lamination from a head is a good tape scratcher. Any drive in reasonable repair will not have a sharp edge in the tape path (or anywhere else). The next condition in a test is the length of tape. For example, there was one drive which wouldn't make more than 1,000 full reel passes, but it read two one-inch records 120,000 times. To read a full reel of tape 120,000 times would have taken over 12,000 hours or over a year of steady running. The drive would not last that long. What testing has been done on the subject, seems to indicate that a test section greater than 10 feet long is a reasonable test section. Just to be sure, the author chose a test section of 100 feet. We felt that this was long enough to get the tape through all the parts of the drive, and generate what loose oxide would be generated. Then the tape was written, and a repeated read operation was begun on the 100-foot section. After the test had begun, the drive was never cleaned again. No tape was worn out in less than 20,000 passes over the head. To extrapolate this to full reel passes, it would take more than a year of continuous running to wear out a full reel of the worst case we ever saw.

Now the computer room manager will say to this, "Oh Yeah." He knows that he has worn out tape before this. His tape became useless before 20,000 passes, but not because it was worn out. Tape is usually damaged before 20,000 passes. It may be damaged by the machine, by the operators, or by humidity-temperature cycling. From a computer room standpoint, it doesn't matter.

## tape damage

Catastrophic damage to the tape can be caused by the tape drive pulling the tape apart. Tape can be broken by pinch rollers pulling at the tape at one time. During high-speed rewind, if one reel decides to stop before the other reel, tape would not stand the strain. These causes of damage are dealt with in the individual chapters on capstans and reel design. Basically, this type of damage can only be eliminated with good design. The most common cause of short tape life is dirt.

Dirt is here defined as any extraneous particle that can become embedded in the mag tape. The term foreign particle would not apply here. If the oxide of the tape is scrapped up in a little ball and becomes embedded in a tape, that's dirt. But it certainly isn't foreign material. In general, the dirt that does become embedded in the tape is displaced material from other parts of the reel.

When evaluating a drive, it is a good thing to notice where oxide dust can collect. Notice any pressure pads that might cause an abnormal vertical force to the tape. Dust pockets and high vertical forces are excellent dirt generators.

It should be pointed out that tape rubbing lightly against a surface does not generate dust. Magnetic oxide dust only is generated when the force holding the tape to the surface is high. Oxide dust is generated under pressure pads. For example, if tape is wrapped around a fixed guide, look for lots of dust just before it passes by the capstan. The magnetic head is a good dust generator when a high normal force causes oxide to rub off the tape.

Some of the binder comes with the oxide. Once the dust gets too high, it is forced back into the tape and the binder seems to make a little glob. Once this happens, the tape is on the way to the trash can. A glob of dirt on a tape will lift the rest of the tape away from the magnet head. Studies have shown that a 0.0004 inch head-to-tape separation is enough to reduce the signal 50 percent. A glob of dirt makes a record unreadable.

## tape cleaners

Any drive will generate some oxide dust. However, some drives aggravate the situation by providing collection centers for oxide particles. A good collection center is a tape cleaner. There are several cleaners in use now. Most operators feel that the cleaner adds considerably to tape life. One user backspaced tape twice after a tape error rather than only once. This caused the error record to be passed over the tape cleaner before it was read again. He felt that this worked much better than just backspacing once and re-reading. The author does not have test results to prove that a tape cleaner increases tape life. However, I have never heard anyone who felt that tape cleaner shortened tape life. And I have heard many who swear by the cleaners. It is a very difficult thing to evaluate because of the long life of tape, with or without a cleaner.

## good housekeeping

No single device, or lack of one, will have as much effect on your tape life as good housekeeping. Keep the drives clean, and the room clean. Any drive will generate dirt. This should be swept away. Any drive takes air from the room and passes it over the tape. Keep the room clean and less dirt will be seen by the tape. It is customary to clean drives after each eight-hour shift. Drives should be cleaned whenever there is a major change in programs. Certainly the drives should be cleaned at the lunch break, as well as at the change of shift. Good housekeeping pays off in longer tape life and fewer tape errors.

## reel loss

We can store a great deal of information on a reel of magnetic tape. With an inefficient record length, a reel of magnetic tape can keep a 1,000-line-a-minute printer working a half-hour. And if a reel of tape gets lost or destroyed, we have lost a great deal of information. Consequently, we should consider carefully what to do when a reel is lost. Eventually it is going to happen; no one can put human beings in any system over a long period of time and not lose a reel. The reel may be misplaced, stolen, or damaged by fire or handling. Eventually it is going to happen. Fireproof vaults for the most valued reels are an excellent way of putting off the day when fire damages our reels of tape (see Fig. 58). Storing duplicate information in a second location is another popular means of insuring that information doesn't get lost. But don't let yourself be led down the path that it won't ever happen. Fireproof vaults, duplication of information, and a good labeling system will put off the day. But it is a matter of degree, some day a whole reel of information will be lost, and the duplicate can't be found because it was destroyed also. Consider now what you should do when it does happen.

## computer room logistics

The computer room becomes the center of information. Data is fed into the room, and after processing, the data is sent out. Many times this information is brought in and taken out with reels of tape. And certainly a computer installation is constantly eating more tape. Make

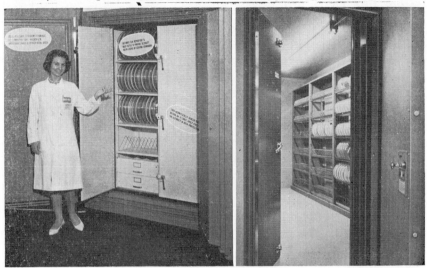

**Fig. 58—FIRE RESISTANT DATA VAULTS.** Here are two types of tape storage that are resistant to the effects of fire. Both vaults have insulation to keep the tapes cool during a fire. A reel of tape can hold 25 million characters of valuable information. Even a small fire can destroy a reel. *Courtesy Data American Engineering Company.*

sure that the computer room has good access to delivery service. Because of the value of the tape and its information, tape reels should not be left lying around a mailroom. Also, as shown in Chapter 2, temperature cycling can lead to tape damage. Whenever tape is received, it should be dispatched directly to the computer room environment for storage. Once the tape is sent out of the computer room, it should be dispatched directly to its destination. The only safe place to store tape is in a computer tape vault, not in a mailroom bag.

## catastrophic loss

The fire in the Pentagon in 1959 probably helped industry more than it harmed the Department of Defense. No computer site has forgotten that it can happen here. When choosing a tape drive, some thought should be given to "What if it does happen here?" How soon can my manufacturer replace the drives that I buy? Are there other machines in the area that I can use while my machine is being repaired?

When choosing special features for our tapes, consider how these might make you compatible with other computers in the area that you may want to use. The advantage to a feature may be so great that noncompatibility is a small price.

## power line considerations

Almost all tape transports depend on the power company for good speed control. The frequency of the power, usually 60 cycles per second, controls the speed of the tape-off over the head. If the frequency of the power changes, the tape speed changes. You may think that the incoming frequency is perfect. Indeed, an electric clock says the frequency is very good. However electric clocks work on the average. At the end of any 24-hour period, the power company can speed up or slow down to make the clocks right. Over a 24-hour period, the frequency is perfect, but in any short-term period like one minute, the frequency may be off. How far off depends on the source of power. If the power comes from large public power sources, the variation is most likely plus or minus 0.5 cycles. If our source of power is a local generating station not tied into a larger system, frequency may change as much as 1 or 2 cycles per second. Each cycle per second is 1.7 percent variation. If the power changes by as much as 1 cycle per second, check with the drive manufacturer to be sure that we can still write tape that can be read. If the tape is written when the frequency is 1.7 percent low, and read when the frequency is 1.7 percent high, the effects are additive. Data frequency appears to the drive as coming in at 3.4 percent fast. The tape system may not be able to stand that much additional speed variation.

## summary

As you may already have guessed, the allied areas of concern cannot be taken care of with one short review. These areas of concern require constant review. Because of program changes or company changes, any system may run down. It is our problem to see that each of the allied areas contributes to the tape system efficiency. If a careful review of the allied areas is part of our routine, 95 percent of our tape drive problems will take care of themselves.

## CHAPTER 8. Questions

1. What does KC or KB rates mean?
2. What is the Peak Rate of a drive?
3. What is the Effective Rate of a drive?
4. What is the Day Rate of a drive?
5. Describe two ways of measuring the inter-record gap on tape.
6. What are three causes of long inter-record gaps on tape?
7. Describe the data that must be gathered to measure the effectiveness of a tape system.
8. What are three problems in storage of magnetic tape?

# 9 trends

**WHERE DID TAPE DRIVES COME FROM** and where are they going? Many patents that affect tape drives have long since run out. These patents were taken out for the mechanism that is used to transport movie film from one reel to another. The mechanisms have much in common with tape transports. The idea that a tape drive was needed on a computer seems to have originated with the fountainhead of most computer ideas, Von Neumans. In his original work on digital computers, reference is made to tape recorders. Audio wire recorders were popular about this time—in fact, wire recorder spools can still be purchased.

The need for the original wire recorders was a long-term store, an extension of memory. These two reasons are as valid today and as important as they were in 1946. Tape recorders are simply a long-term store, and an extension of memory.

Of course this really doesn't say very much. A punch card, or a typewritten message is also long-term store, or an extension of memory. What are the important characteristics of a tape, or wire recorder, that makes it almost indispensible to a computer?

## tape drive assets

Writing out to a tape drive is fast. A computer can write a record to a drive and have the entire operation completed in 15 milliseconds. That means that a computer can write records on tape at the frequency of electrical power coming out of wall plugs. The reason we don't see fluorescent lamps go on and off is that the lenses of our eyes cannot change as quickly as the rays of the fluorescent lighting do. However, a computer is able to write records faster than the eye can follow.

By comparison, let us consider a high-speed printer. If a high-speed printer lists at 1,000 lines per minute, it will list 16.7 lines per second. When a tape drive is working at its most inefficient rate, it will list 3.5 times as much information.

The second big advantage of a tape drive becomes apparent— ability to read back at the same rate. Once a printer has listed out its information, it cannot recall the data except through the tortuous means of keypunching and re-entry. A tape drive is fast and it can read and write fast.

The third advantage to a tape drive is removable media and a high volumetric efficiency; that is, we can store a reel of tape in a small place. Magnetic disks also have the advantage of fast input and output. But all the information on a disk could be stored in two or three reels of tape which could be hidden in the disk mechanism.

All the files that have been manufactured couldn't hold the information that is stored in one large user's vault. So a tape drive stores a lot of information in a small volume.

The above three reasons were probably why wire recorders were specified for the first digital computers. You could write out fast, re-read the information fast, and store it in demountable, small packages. These three reasons are going to keep tape drives with us for a long time. No device on the horizon appears to come anywhere near replacing all the characteristics of a tape drive. So let us go on, to see where we are going and how other devices compare with tape drives.

## what's available in tape drives?

At the present time there are a number of drives available to the computer user. Many times he is not free to choose the drive that fits his needs, because the computer manufacturer generally specifies what drive will be used on his computer. However, the tape drive problem and the cost of the tape drives make tape drive consideration a pretty big tail. So a little wagging of the dog is in order. Computers should be chosen as much for the tape drives as they are for the computer. In fact, it is this author's opinion that a computer system should be chosen more on the basis of input-output equipment than it is for the computer itself. The transistors and cores from any manufacture will build a fine central processor. But there are some tape drives that work it into our installation very well. Figure 59 (page 130) shows some of the tape transports available.

A listing of many of the speeds and densities of the present day transports shows that 36 to 150 inches covers the range of most speeds. And 100 to 1,200 bits per inch covers the range of most densities. Since IBM has the lion's share of the computer market, their speeds and densities are the most popular. The 200, 555, and 800 bits per inch are the predominant IBM tape drive densities. And 37.5, 75, and 112 inches per second are the predominant speeds. Many other manufacturers have adopted the IBM densities in order to be compatible. Some manufacturers have even adopted IBM speeds. However, many have succumbed

to the temptation to increase the speeds of the drive in order to have a better transfer rate than IBM has.

## future developments

Where can we go from here? As you well know, it is dangerous to set a limit on any development. As soon as we set a limit on how fast or how far we can go, someone comes along and does better. Even with these perils, it is well to set down some tentative limits as road markers. In each case that a limit is set, it is accompanied with the reasons for the limit. Once a reason is made invalid the limit will go.

## density of recording

The first limit on where we are going is the recording density. The limiting factor on this is the ability of the reading system to resolve separate bits on tape. As density of recordings go higher, one bit tends to wash out the previous bits recorded. Therefore, the signal played back moves and is diminished by new information recorded. It is even possible to write information on tape so dense that the tape is not saturated. Once magnetic tape is not saturated, readback system has lost a touchstone. The saturation of tape during the recording process allowed the electronics great freedom for variation in parameters. If the recording system electronics became too strong, the tape was saturated and didn't respond to overdrive. Saturation recording keeps us from worrying about circuit drift. In saturation recording we magnetize the tape all the way plus some more. However, saturation recording is limited.

Saturation recording is limited by how small the effective head gap can be made. It is limited by how short the ratio of the length of magnetic spots on the tape is to their width and depth. Thinner oxide layers would tend to allow denser magnetic recording. Thinner oxide layers would also reduce the signal.

Because of the mechanical problem in the design of effective head gaps (due to the thickness of the oxide on tape), and because of the effects one bit has on another, the author would put an upper limit on saturation recording at 3,000 bits per inch. This does not say that someone in a lab can not record at a high density, or that the industry will never record commercial information at higher densities. It does say

←———

**Fig. 59**—COMMERCIAL TAPE DRIVES. Some of the many currently available commercial tape drives. Speed ranges are 75 ips to 150 ips. Three types of buffer storage are used: arms, air storage and loose bin. Pictured, left to right: Ampex Company, Control Data Corporation, Cook Electric Company, GE Computer Department, International Business Machines Corporation, Midwestern Instruments.

that a different approach is needed before more than 3,000 bits per inch are possible in everyday computer usage.

It is immediately obvious that the nonsaturating recording is already going well beyond 3,000 bits per inch. However, for computers this is a new technology. It will require new types of head design, new types of tapes, and maybe new methods of recording. It certainly will require more stable circuits for reading and writing.

## tape speed

The next consideration is how fast the tapes will be moved over the heads. What is the limit? As far as we can tell now, there is no limit. Tape could be moved over a head so fast that it would burn out the head if they came into contact. At high speeds, an air film develops to prevent head contact.

As tape moves faster and faster there are other limits, First, of course, is the inter-record gap. As speeds get higher, the gaps tend to get bigger; this reduces the Effective rate, which defeats the purpose of high speeds. Also, at high speeds the drives go through a reel of tape so fast that load-unload time becomes more significant. This in turn reduces the Day rate, which again reduces and defeats the purpose of high speeds. It is something like driving your car fast on city streets. The faster you drive, the quicker you will get across the city. But the traffic lights and the traffic make higher and higher speeds not worth the trouble. There are presently some drives that move tape at 150 inches per second. It looks as if we won't be moving tape in a tape drive much faster than 200 inches per second for some time.

## tape width

The industrial standard on width is half-inch tape. However, tape is manufactured much wider, and can be obtained 24 inches wide. There is no reason that a drive couldn't be designated one, two, three, or four inches wide. I have little doubt that some day a drive using four-inch tape will be designed. However, for a time it appears that there will be few drives which use tape wider than one inch. It appears that whatever gain could be obtained by going wider can also be gained by recording denser, or putting the recording tracks closer together. Most drives will continue to use half-inch tape. The ASA standard for communication interchange is half-inch tape. However, there will be more and more high performance drives which use one-inch tape widths. And of course, there will be a few which use even wider tape. From a practical standpoint, one-inch tape can be considered the maximum for now.

## number of tracks

The new ASA standard specifies nine tracks for half-inch tape. This is not a theoretical limit. It seems possible that we could put many more tracks on a half-inch tape. However, manufacturing problems become more difficult, and the signal read from the tape is reduced. Also, as the track widths are reduced to allow more tracks, the tolerance on tape width becomes more significant. Just because ASA has established nine tracks for half-inch tape, eighteen tracks for one-inch tape sounds like a good number. However, error correction codes and additional clock tracks make 23 to 24 tracks on a one-inch tape look more reasonable. This again is another number which has no theoretical limit, but is a manufacturing and tolerance limit.

## to sum up

We have reviewed all the factors that will go to make up the tape drive of the future. Only one of the number has a technical limit; this is density. The other limits were soft limits. You could go farther, but it just doesn't seem reasonable at this time. To summarize:

| Item | Valve | Type of Limitation |
|---|---|---|
| Recording density | 3,000 bits/inch | Technical, head resolving tape saturating problem |
| Tape speed | 200 inches/sec. | Soft limit, could be faster but is it worth it? |
| Tape width | 1 inch | Soft limit, could be wider but will only be worth it in special cases |
| Transfer rate | 1,200 KC (eight-bit characters) characters) 19,200 KB (bit rate) | |
| No of tracks on tape | 23, (16 information) | Soft limit |

In other words, the author is predicting a 1.2 MC (mega-cycle) and 19.2 MB (mega-bit) transfer rate as the upper limit of saturation recording. Once more, the polished door knob on my den says that it will be here in five years. Is this the ultimate? No!

## future after five years

This is the limit of saturation recording. It seems to me that the next technological breakthrough in tape drives will be an electronic one. Most of the breakthrough up to this point has been mechanical.

Actuators were made to move faster. The reel drives were made to stand more heating effects. Accuracy in guiding improved to allow higher density. Head and tape manufacture improved to allow still more accurate higher-density recording.

The ideal tape drive would move tape at 10 inches per second, record a million frames per inch on half-inch wide tape. Why? The slow speed would make all mechanical problems insignificant. The high recording density would give a good transfer rate, and a high volumetric storage. The half-inch width would allow greater length without exceed· ing the human weight restriction on how big a reel should be. There are others who would put other dimensions on the ideal drive. However, no one would disagree with a million frames per second except to increase the number even more. How do we do it?

We must go to nonsaturation recording. This is the recording tech- nique which is used in audio-tape recorders and most analog recorders. This requires a technological breakthrough in electronics. The write circuits and the read circuits must develop a long-term stability that they do not now possess.

The author is therefore predicting a constant series of improvements in transfer rates. There is no real limit to what a tape drive will record. There will be plateaus of progress, but never a complete stop.

So much for transfer rates. What other trends are appearing in the industry?

### load-unload improvements

One can almost go back to the chart in Figure 56 and predict the improvements. Where is time being lost in the tape reel cycle? The first time up is load, unload, and rewind time. IBM is already offering semi- automatic loading and unloading. We will see more of this. In fact there will be fully automatic loading and unloading. Automatic libraries of tape will be under computer control. Off-tape drive rewind is coming. Whenever we look at a drive rewinding tape, we should ask how much of that machine capability is being utilized at the moment. We will have to answer, "very little." A tape drive rewind tape is like a bulldozer plowing a garden. Both machines can do their respective jobs, but neither is very well matched. Once, the industry solves the problem of demounting two reels at once, more off-drive rewinding will begin to take place. Cartridges are coming.

### effective transfer rates

Next on the chart is Data time. There doesn't appear that there will be much change in Data time. Higher rates will tend to reduce data time, and generate more gaps on a reel. However, bigger memories will tend to allow the recording of more information in a block. The two tendencies will more or less cancel out. To the extent that the two tendencies do not cancel out, progress in transfer rate is held back. It makes no sense to record at high densities, and have the effect lost in poor data length due to poorer data-length-to-record gap ratio. We must record more information in a record in order to utilize the higher densities of recording.

## tape system idle time

Tape System Idle time was made up of two elements. One was that the computer couldn't use more than one or two drives at one time. The other element was that the inter-record gaps used up time between records. The computers are going to reduce the first elements. Computers will reduce Idle time by reading or writing more drives in parallel. There will be more computer cross baring. That is, one channel will be able to get at any drive on the computer. Drive A may work into channel 1 for this record reading. However, for the next record channel 1 is busy, so Drive A will be automatically switched to channel 2. This will reduce Computer Idle time. At present, it frequently happens that eight to ten drives are connected into one computer channel. It frequently happens in sorting that the computer wants to write on two of the drives in one string on one channel. The hardware requires that the writing take place serially. First write on one drive, and then write on the second drive. With a cross-bar system, eight or ten drives are not connected into one computer channel. Eight or ten drives are associated with two or three computer channels. A computer can therefore get at any drive as long as the drive is not busy and a computer channel is free.

The second element in Computer Idle time is the size of the inter-record gap. No special breakthroughs are needed to do this. Just many little details have to be cleaned up. Work is being done here, and results will be evident.

## tape usage

The amount of tape used is strictly a function of the user. A number of studies have been made to indicate that many installations do not use more than 30 or 40 feet of a reel. This of course turns out to be a gigantic waste. If one is only using 30 feet of tape on a reel, consideration should be given to using a disk, a drum, or a tape loop. A tape drive is designed to handle large amounts of data. And 30 or 40 or 150 feet are not large amounts of data by tape drive standards. This need for small demountable storage is the motivation behind removable magnetic disk, and tape loop machines. Look for development of a cheap small-reel tape drive. Thirty or 40 feet of tape will be reasonable on this machine.

## asa code

The American Standards Association has recently established a Code for Interchange of Information. (ASCII) This code will apply to various media, punched cards, paper tape, and magnetic tape. ASCII on magnetic tape is to be recorded on nine channels. There were good reasons for increasing the number from the traditional seven. Most important, the traditional seven channels would not handle ASCII and carry a parity bit along. This meant that at least an eight-channel tape was required. Any change from the seven-track tape was a serious one. And it didn't matter so much what we changed to, as it did that the number was being changed. It was important to add still another track, for a total of nine, so that higher density recording became possible. This requires a little explanation.

ASCII requires seven bits. Seven bits will define 128 different characters. Since there are only 10 numerics, most of the defined characters are nonnumerics. But in business and a scientific work, most of the data that the computer deals with is numeric. Consequently, the X3.2 committee thought it would be very wise if two numbers could be written instead of just one X3.2 character. For the case where all the data is numbers, a numeric-pack would double the effective recording density. Numerics requires four bits. Four and four are still eight, plus a parity bit, makes nine. So as long as seven-track tapes had to go, nine-track rather than eight-track tape was preferred.

Also, the ninth track had another advantage. The theory of tape recording says that if you can predict the starting of a character on tape, you can double the recording density. In the present seven-channel tape, the tape controller does not know just when the character begins. The controller has to wait for the first "one" bit, and then it assumes the rest of the bits will be in the "X" microseconds. But the one bit just received may have been the end of the character, and all the rest of the characters were zeros. The controller has no way of knowing. So the addition of a bit that always comes at the beginning or the end of the character will remove doubt as to just where the character is. It is something like trying to find your wife's favorite cooking pan after a church potluck supper. If someone would just tell you where the cake pans begin, where the bean pots begin, and where the salad bowls begin, you could find her casserole dish much faster. So it is with tape drive controllers, a clock track which indicates exactly where the character begins will allow the controller to work much faster. And as soon as the controller can work faster, the recording density can be increased. A clock track will allow double the recording density.

## nine-channel summary

Six information channels were not enough to handle ASCII. Once a departure was made from six information channels, eight channels seems the best choice. Eight channels would handle ASCII and leave a spare information channel. This spare information channel can be used for a numeric pack, or for a clock track, to allow higher density recording.

## meaning to user

What does this standard code mean to the user? It means that eventually our files are going to be rewritten. This is normal for any magnetic tape file anyway. It is just a matter of time before it would be done, whether a new standard comes out or not. The new standard may hurry us along as to when we want the file rewritten. And the last six words are the key: "when we want the file rewritten." The ASA standard does not require that we change over. Indeed there is no reason why we can't continue to use a seven-track tape until we retire. Just as there is no law that requires Ford to use standard nuts in his automobile. But he does. He does because the standard is good. And the standard is cheaper and more available. When a customer needs a repair nut in Toband Falls, Montana, he wants the standard. Similar reasons will cause us to have our tape file rewritten.

The industry is standardizing on nine-track tape for information interchange. Some day, we will want to send our Social Security and Income Tax reports into the government on magnetic tape. The ASA standard will be the preferred method. Presently, the seven-track IBM's tape is accepted by these agencies for reporting of income information. It is presumed that they will continue to accept tape in this format for some time to come. However, eventually, like the horseshoe, seven-track tape will become a relic. Don't be the last one to change over.

There are other immediate gains. If ours is a normal installation, the numeric pack mode will increase our transfer rate. If we happen to be using more than 64 characters, ASCII will allow us to reduce the code representation to one frame on tape. The immediate gains are important; the eventual gains are necessary.

The numeric pack mode has a second benefit. This mode puts twice the information in the same length of tape, twice the density—therefore, only half the length of tape. Now wouldn't it be nice to reduce the number of reels of tape by one half? We might be able to stop buying reels for a while, as we use the tape saved from higher packing densities.

## low cost drives

Most of the writing in this book has been about faster transfer rate machines. Don't overlook the low transfer rate machines. Some day, someone will come out with a new low-cost, low-performance tape drive. When this happens, a whole new world of tape usage will open up to the computer user.

When this elusive low-cost transport is finally invented, the number that can be used reach into the hundred of thousands. Anyone who has a cash register will want to record every transaction on magnetic tape. Let the computer analyze the cash flow. Since the time is also recorded on the tape the computer can also analyze customer buying time. Anyone who has a scale will want the weight recorded on magnetic, so that the inventory can be updated directly from the data on the magnetic tape. Anyone who has a counter, counting anything, will want the count written on magnetic tape for automatic data processing.

There are already some attempts to reach this market. See Figure 60 for some low-cost tape drives. These are notable efforts in the

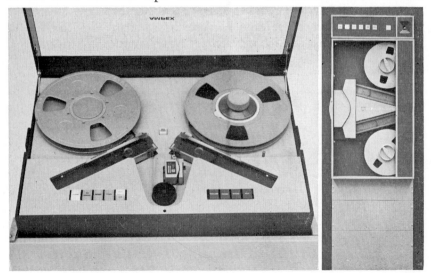

**Fig. 60**—LOW COST DRIVES. Here are two notable examples of lower cost drives. Courtesy Ampex Company and Datamec Corporation.

direction of low-cost drives. However notable, these drives are *not* the low-cost ones that I'm speaking about. The drive that I'm speaking about must rent for $30 a month with electronics. I'm sure that there are some designers who will say that this is ridiculous. But even he would agree that a drive that rents for $30 a month will reach the mass market.

Let me spend a moment describing *the* low cost drive. First of all, the drive will record serially on tape. It will do this not to conserve tape width, but to conserve electronics. At the present time, a big problem in low cost drives is the cost of the electronics. Many times, the cost of the electronics equals or exceeds the cost of the mechanism.

One way to reduce the cost of the electronics is to eliminate them. Therefore, the low-cost drive will record serial. Not completely serial! There will be two tracks on tape. One will be the clock track, and the other will be the data track. It is agreed that lower cost could be obtained by recording both the clock and the data on the same track. However, recording two-track allows the tape to be read back on the computer center's normal drives. A single-track recording would not allow such compatibility.

A low-cost drive might record at a fairly high density. This is to reduce tape usage, and to eliminate the need for reel service. If the drive is recording at a high density, little tape movement is needed to record a transaction or a count. With little tape movement, buffer storage and high powered reel drives are eliminated. "The stretch of the

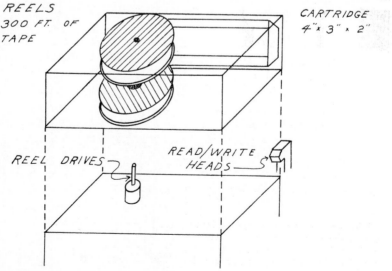

**Fig. 61—DREAMERS LOW COST DRIVE.** This is my pet project on what a low cost drive should be.

tape becomes the buffer storage" (quoted from chapter 1). Whether this design or some other design comes along, low cost is coming. When it comes, every counting, weighing and or automatic measuring device becomes an input device to the computer. (For dreamers, see Figure 61 for my idea of a low-cost tape drive.)

## tape loop recorders

NASA and the military have for some time been orbiting tape recorders. These devices have been used to record information picked up by the satellite as it is orbiting the earth. Then on command, the recorder speeds up, and plays back all the information previously recorded. As far as I know, these recorders are loop recorders. That is, the tape is made into a continuous loop and feeds back upon itself. The advantage of this, of course, is that no reverse or rewind is needed, as mounting or demounting is not allowed in orbit.

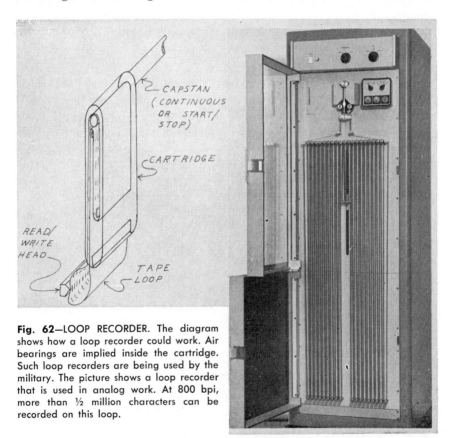

**Fig. 62—LOOP RECORDER.** The diagram shows how a loop recorder could work. Air bearings are implied inside the cartridge. Such loop recorders are being used by the military. The picture shows a loop recorder that is used in analog work. At 800 bpi, more than ½ million characters can be recorded on this loop.

One might look upon this type of drive as a long narrow drum. Or again, it might be thought of as a disk storage unit reworked into a cylinder. (See Fig. 62.) Is a loop recorder of any use to us? Yes, yes, yes, YES! Let us for a moment compare a tape *loop* recorder with a disk. The tape loop recorder can record all the information that a disk can record. But since it is dealing with tape instead of a disk surface, more length of oxide is in front of the recorded head. Since tape is a pliable medium, the tape can be folded over on itself for compact storage. With compact storage comes the possibility of many loops, and easy removal. Also, tape loop recorders have one advantage that only the NASA and the military have used. The tape loop has much lower mass than a disk, or drum. This means that the speed can be changed rapidly.

NASA uses this speed change ability to cause the information that was recorded in 90 minutes or so of earth orbit to play back in seconds. Such time compression has been used in industry also. For example, data that comes in on a communication line will frequently come in at 110 bits per second. After the communication is received, a time compression would allow the data to be dumped into the computer at 120 KB. In a similar way, information could be taken out of a computer at 120 KB and then expanded to 110 bits per second. The low mass of a tape loop recorder would allow time compression and expansion.

Tape loop recorders will be in competition with the removable disk storage units. And the tape loops recorders will be exploiting the low mass advantage to do things that a disk or drum could never do. Figure 63 (page 142) shows a tape random access device. However, the advantages of tape is not lost.

## incremental drives

There is another form of digital tape transport. This is the incremental drive. Up to now, all the drives have been described as having a constantly moving media during the recording or playback process. An incremental drive gets around this problem. The tape on an incremental drive will move a small (0.005 inches) amount under command. It will then stop and wait for the next character or command. Such a drive is nonsynchronous. It does not depend on an exact time relationship for its recording and playback. This drive makes an ideal communications line transmitter and receiver. The drive can transmit with complete submission to the needs of the communication lines. If the communication lines has a three-second dropout, the tape drive can stop and wait, without pain, with no problem.

It might be interesting to review how such a drive operates (see Fig. 28). Incremental tape drives are not inherently cheap. They have most of the functions of a conventional tape drive plus the incremental function. The incremental function is needed so that the drive can record a single character upon demand of the communication line. In communications line work, and other applications where demand recording is necessary, low cost incremental tape recorders are now in

**Fig. 63**—A RANDOM TAPE DRIVE. This tape drive uses short strips of tape (about 15 ft.) to record data. The tape is pulled off each small reel by a pinch roller and capstan. *Courtesy AB Atvidabergs Industrier, Sweden.*

competition with paper tape. Tape loop recorders may be competitive in some applications, some day. This is especially true if loop recorders ever go incremental, as I am sure they will.

## tape drives and communication

At this point, it might be well to discuss the subject that has been refered to for several paragraphs—communication work. At the present time, communication on commercial transmission lines is dominated by paper tape readers and punches. Paper tape readers and punches have three big advantages, (1) they are low cost, (2) they are incremental, (3) they match communication lines' speeds very well. It might be argued that the communication lines were made to match the speeds of the readers and punches. Whatever the reason, communication lines and paper tape seem to go very well together.

When an installation has a message to send, it will generally first punch the information into a paper tape. Then the paper tape is fed into a sender for transmission to a remote location. Several elements are involved here. First of all, the information is first stored in paper tape. Then it is transmitted on the communication line at a different rate than it was punched. Finally, the paper tape may stop and go as the occasion demands. In most installations, the tape stops and goes because of mechanical reading.

Electronics can do every one of these functions. Indeed, there are a number of communication computers which have replaced paper tape installations. The speed of a computer does not match communication line speeds very well. However, multiplexing makes the match much better. Multiplexing is a process which causes the computer to spend a little time (five microseconds) with one communication line and then go on to the next communication line.

Back one paragraph, it takes little imagination to see that we could cover the paper tape with oxide. Then we could magnetize instead of punch. And magnetic tape drives could directly replace paper tape communication line work. What is the hitch? The hitch is—the first advantage of paper tape. A digital magnetic tape drive is too expensive. A magnetic tape drive can be made incremental, and it can be made to match communication lines. But a magnetic tape drive is more expensive, right now. And, it offers few advantages that aren't already inherent in a paper tape system.

But what about this new device, the communication processor? Here magnetic tape drives may have an advantage which paper tape can't match. Communication processors are making higher speed transmissions economically feasable. Without a communication processor, it is difficult to get enough information in front of a high-speed channel to keep the channel busy. A computer generally has the other problem, where do we get a channel that can give or take enough information fast enough? So computers will be working at a higher transmission rates. And what is to receive at these high transmission rates? Right now the only answer is another computer. Someday, it may well be a magnetic tape drive which is operating at a higher data rate than a paper tape can reach.

Also, these communication lines magnetic tape drives may utilize the low mass to compress time and match a computer to slow speed lines Figure 64 shows such a drive. The left head could record information that is transmitted. The right head would then read and transmit the information at a much higher rate. This sort of arrangement has another advantage. If the computer were the device recording the information in the first place, multiplexing would not be necessary. Any multiple-plexing that a computer does takes computer time and memory. If the

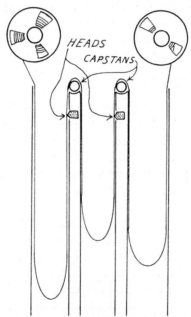

**Fig. 64—TWO SPEED DRIVES.** This is a tape drive that can operate in two speeds at one time. One speed can be incremental and the other synchronous. Such a drive has been marketed in the analog field.

computer can be relieved of the multiplexing job, more communication lines can be serviced with the same computer.

We are going to see more special purpose magnetic tape drives in the communication field.

### specialized tape drives

The final trend in the tape drive field is peculiar. The peculiar needs of the communication field are an example of the many that will be seen. If we look at the tape drives presently on the market, they are all very much alike. They read at X speed, backspace at X speed, and rewind at 3X speed. They all make provisions for the IBM reel or the NAB reel.

Ninety-nine and 44/100 percent of the tape drives make provision for one write head and one read head just behind. Most auto manufacturers have more styles of station wagons than we have styles of tape drives. One of the big reasons for this is that the industry is young. Another is that the tape drive is wedded to the computer which hasn't allowed much time for specialties. But in the maturity of the second, third, or fourth generation computers, there will be time for specialties.

Tape drives are going to become stylized, to the particular needs of the user.

## slow or incremental backspace

A different speed backspace can have many useful applications. With this type of drive, tape would move in the reverse direction a third or tenth the speed that it does in the forward direction. A computer would write or read in the forward direction. However, the slower and cheaper off-line device would read and write from the same drive, but in reverse. Surprisingly, most of the present-day tape drives could be made to read faster in the forward direction, if backspacing were made slower.

## portable recorders

Portable recorders are coming. Here are some of the possibilities. Service personnel could take the recorder to a troublesome machine and monitor control lines with a time base. A computer program would read in the tape records, analyze and print out or plot the results. Parts of a chemical or power plant could be monitored in a similar way. If the recorders are very light-weight, meter readers would record reading directly on tape for computer processing. As far as I can tell, this project and the one above are awaiting an expressed market need. No technological breakthroughs are needed for the developments.

## convenience items

Quick release reel hubs are coming, and are here. From the discussion of Chapter 8, it is apparent that much time is spent screwing and unscrewing reel hubs. Someone is going to develop a quick release reel hub. The time that an operator spends mounting the reel will be drastically decreased. Also, he won't have to be so careful about aligning the reel on the drive. The quick release hub will be self-aligning.

Cartridge loading and unloading is already with us in IBM's Hypertape. This feature will come into the lower cost transports also.

The ASA standard format does not make provisions for this type of loading and unloading. More than one ASA standard is possible.

## more rugged tape

With serial—and probably portable—recording, look for more easily handled tape. Presently it is well to have clean hands and a clean room

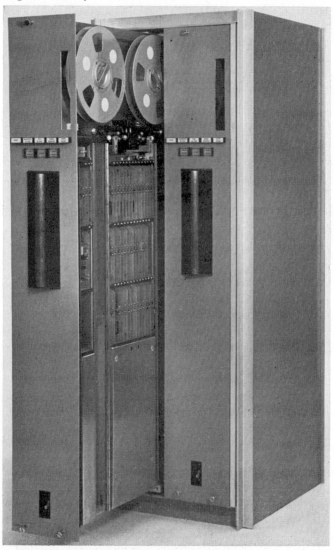

**Fig. 65**—RUGGEDIZED DRIVE. This SCEL tape drive is an excellent example of what can be done to ruggedize a tape drive. This drive is designed for the military to operate on a truck under field conditions. It operates at 150 ips. *Courtesy Ampex Corporation.*

wherever a tape drive will be working. A stock room doesn't necessarily have either condition. Therefore, more drives will be designed to operate in a more difficult environment. Ability to operate in a more difficult environment will be transferred over to the big tape drives too. As computers switch over from germanium transistors to silicon, the need for room air-conditioning will be reduced. Only the tape drive will not be designed to operate in a normal, dusty, humid, atmosphere. See Figure 65 for a tape drive design for the military to cope with battlefield environment. Many small computer users can't afford fancy air-conditioning. So the tape drives will go with the computer, into the atmosphere people have been using all the time.

## tape drives vs. disks

The differences between sequential type machines tape drives, and random machines, disks, is a matter of degree. The sequential machines do have some control over the next record available by backspacing, going forward or skipping. The random machines do not have complete control over which will be the next record on the track. They must wait for the disk to turn to the desired location. I have seen computer programs run that made a tape drive look like a small disk to the computer. Disk and tapes are different in degree not in fundamental purpose.

Random input-output devices have a relatively short time between reading any given record, and reading the next randomly selected record. Sequential devices have a relatively long time between the reading of a record and reading the next randomly selected record. This time is so long that the operation is built around the device and sequential processing is done.

It sometimes appears to me that there is something in the American Spirit which resents restrictions, no matter how reasonable or useful. Many of the random programs that I have seen would run faster and cheaper by batch processing. However, the user chose to use the random device. One might think that because I am writing a book on "Digital Tape Drives" that I am prejudiced toward tape drives. The same thought has occurred to me. Therefore, I checked with some people who were not writing books on "Digital Tape Drives." They had made the same observations. There are jobs that have been put on random input-output devices that could be done faster and cheaper on sequential devices.

The reason random processing may be slower is the time between the reading of one record and the reading of a second random record. This time may range from 200 MS to 600 MS. And of course in that time a sequential device can read 20 to 60 records. The user would be well advised to analyze the time of data processing on random devices to determine if a sequential device cannot do the job cheaper and faster.

There are some jobs that must be done on a random device regardless of the time. These are the real time inquiry jobs. If a person is waiting on a telephone or at a counter for an answer, only random processing will give the desired answer. It would be nice to be able to line the customers up on a sequential basis and answer their questions the same way.

## random cost vs. sequential cost

What are the cost differences between random devices and sequential devices?

This is rather a difficult answer to give. It is difficult because we have the problem of again comparing apples and oranges. The only time that we are not comparing apples and oranges is when we cost out our job running on both types of input-output devices. It would be very well for us to keep our subjective feeling well buried. It is very easy for a salesman or consultant to learn that we want random or sequential processing all along. The figures then come out so as to show that the desired way is the cheaper means. As indeed it might be, but then it might not be the economical way to go. If our feelings have played a part, if our emotions have played a part, we will never really know which was best for us. Also, keep in mind that no matter which way we go, the calculation should be repeated periodically. Improvements in the seek time on a disk, or the recording density on tape, can change the answer radically.

One final word of caution—this is an apple and an orange comparison. The figures are useful as a jumping-off point into the consideration between disks and tapes. These figures are the first word, not the last word. Figure 66 shows domains of cost vs. performance for various storage.

For consideration, I would like to suggest a means of comparison for all the devices that could be used to do our processing. Make up a chart with columns as follows:

1. Peak rate has been explained as the maximum rate at which the device can operate.

2. Effective rate is the transfer rate from tape when inter-record gaps are considered. Effective rate from the disks, or other random devices, is the rate when seek time is considered. It may be thought that this places the random device in an unfavorable light. Seek time is long; this makes Effective rates low. This is one of the penalties of

random devices. In many jobs, the fact that the next record is random more than makes up for the low Effective rate.

3. Maximum access time to any record. In this column, the random devices will show up very well against tape drives.

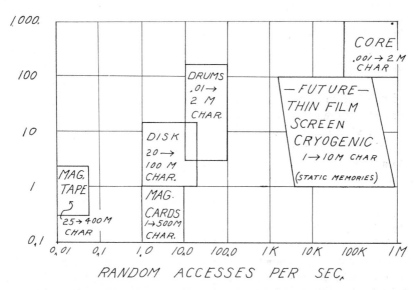

*COST/*
*ON LINE*
*CHAR.* ɪɴ
*$ 0.001*

**Fig. 66**—COST/PERFORMANCE DOMAINS OF MASS STORAGE. Core Memory is the work horse of modern computers. It is the fastest and most expensive form of storage. Drums are one of the earliest forms of large volume storage. Drum access time is limited by the rotation time of the drum. Disk storage introduced a new era in data processing. For the first time enough data could be stored on line to allow a computer to work in a real time environment. Disk storage gave the system analyst a choice between real time and batch processing. Magnetic Card is a new entry in mass storage. The storage efficiency of this media is very high. A single magnetic card may hold forty million characters. Magnetic Tape is the oldest form of mass storage. It is included here to show that tape does not compare well with random access storage devices. Magnetic tape is two orders of magnitude slower than the slowest disk or magnetic card storage. Magnetic tape should only be used in a random access environment when time is not critical, and random access is not the prime reason for having tape drives. Future Storage Static Memories will fill part of the gap between big expensive core memories and slower disk or drums. The most promising technology seems to be cryogenics, thin film or woven screen memories. *Information Courtesy William J. Broderick, Product Planner for Information Storage.*

4. Day rate has been explained for tape drives. For large nonremovable disks, the Day rate is the same as Effective rate. For the removable disk machines, and random card machines, the Day rate is

essentially taking into account the demount and mount time, the spindle slowdown time, and so forth. It is the total data that can be practically transferred in eight hours, divided by eight hours.

5. Operator time is important so that it will be known how many people will have to service the machine.

6. Total data. This column is the sum total of all the data that can be read or written in an eight-hour day. For disks, this is the storage capacity of the disk. For tape drives it is the total data that is on all the reels that a tape drive system can read in an eight-hour day. Similarly, it is all the data that a removable media device can read in an eight-hour day.

7. System Day rate. This is the sum total of all the data that a system of tape drives or disk or removable media devices, can read or write in one day, divided by the number of drives, and by eight hours. If each drive or unit is alone, and is not associated with a controller or master unit, then the number of units is one.

8. Cost of device. List the figures for each device which is to be considered. After these figures are determined, it is a very easy matter to arrive at the cost per KC or KB of Peak rate (1) Effective rate (2), Day rate (4), and System Day rate (7).

Once we have these figures, we can then start to compare these costs against computer cost. From this analysis we can begin to determine what type of input-output device is best for our company. It will be pretty obvious from the figures that are put in the chart that tape drives have the lowest cost-per-day rate. And tape drives offer the largest selection of data to the computer. Indeed, the entire library of tape is available if it is needed. However, there are real time considerations, special sorting, or programming conditions which warrant investigation of other devices. This chart will help us to understand what it will cost for this real time and special situation.

Because tape drives have a high Effective Transfer Rate, because of the availability of huge amounts of data in tape vaults, because of good storage volume efficiency, tape drives will be with us for a long time. Other devices will continue to chip out a special situation notch here and there. But for the large volume, day in, day out data processing, there is nothing in sight to compete with Digital Tape Drives.

## CHAPTER 9. Questions

1. List the three advantages of tape drives as input-output devices.
2. What is the future of tape drive development?
3. What are the benefits of nine track tape?
4. What is an incremental tape drive?
5. List the advantages of tape drives and magnetic disk.
6. How can the cost between batch and random recording be determined?

# appendix

## tape system analysis

This section describes a means of measuring the performance of the tape system. One man with a stopwatch, a ruler, and a clipboard should arrive at a fairly good estimate of tape system performance (Fig. 67).

The clipboard for each drive would have a chart with headings as follows:

1. Load-Unload. This is measured time.
2. Rewind Time. This is a measured time.
3. Computer Time. This is the time the drive is on line and available to the computer. It is a measured time.
4. Length of Tape Used. This is the length obtained by measuring the tape on the machine reel just before rewind.
5. Utilization Ratio. This is the ratio of written tape versus written tape, plus inter-record gap. The figures in this column can be obtained by developing and measuring lengths of tape or by calculation from the known Effective rate.
6. Data Time. This is the time that the drive is transferring data to the computer. This is a calculated time based on drive speed, length of tape used, and utilization ratio.
7. Drive Idle Time. This is the time the drive is waiting for the operators to put the drive on line. The time is measured.
8. Tape System Idle Time. This is the time that the tape system is waiting for computer commands. This time is obtained by subtracting the totals of all Data Times from the Clock time. (This column would only be used when summarizing all data.)
9. Maintenance Time. This is the time that operators or service personnel are doing any maintenance on the drive.
10. Elapsed Time. This is the Clock Time (real time) that has passed between entries.

Column 8 will have to be modified to fit various configurations. If one system has a single controller which allows simultaneous reads and writes, the totals of all Data Times may equal twice System Time. Thus in #8 (above), one-half of all the Data Time is subtracted from Clock Time to obtain System Idle Time.

## day rate

From above numbers the Day Rate of the tape drive is obtained. The Day Rate is equal to the total of the Data Time, times the Peak

Rate divided by the time of the working day (7, 8, or 12 hours, etc). The Day Rate tells us how fast data goes on or comes off tape when averaged over a working day.

## discussion of results

Little need be said about excess load-unload time that is caused by idle operators. But excess load-unload time may also be caused by too busy operators. In many programs, all the drives rewind at the same

*Drive # 4   75 ips*

| ENTRY NO. | LOAD/UNLOAD TIME | REWIND TIME | COMPUTER TIME | LENGTH OF TAPE USED | UTILIZATION RATIO | DATA TIME | DRIVE IDLE TIME | TAPE SYSTEM IDLE TIME | MAINTENANCE TIME | ELAPSED TIME | COMMENTS |
|---|---|---|---|---|---|---|---|---|---|---|---|
| | 1 | 2 | 3 | 4 | 5 | 6 | 7 | 8 | 9 | 10 | |
| 1 | .7 | | | | | | | | | 9 00 | Reel Stuck |
| 2 | | .5 | 200 | 60% | .3 | | | | | 9,10 | Set # 341 |
| 3 | | 1.5 | | 1500 | 60% | 2.4 | | | | 925 | |
| 4 | .3 | | 25 | | | | | | | 925 | |
| 5 | | | | | | | | | 2 | 927 | Light bulb |
| 6 | | | | | | | 7 | | | 934 | |
| 7 | .2 | | | | | | | | | 934 | Input cards |
| 8 | | 2.0 | 6 | 2000 | 20% | 1.0 | | | | 940 | for job #32 |
| 9 | | | | | | | | 2 | | 942 | Set up #48 |
| 10 | | | | | | | | | | | |
| | 1.2 | 4.0 | 31 | 3700 | — | 3.7 | 9 | | 2 | 42 | |

$$\frac{Data\ Time}{Total\ Time} \times Peak = \frac{3.7}{42} \times 60 KC = \boxed{5.3\ KC}\ _{Day\ Rate}$$

**Fig. 67—CLIP BOARD CHART.** This is the same chart used in Fig. 56. It is repeated here for convenience.

time. Then the operators have eight drives to unload and load. Natural-
ly, the last drive on the string is going to have excess load-unload
time as it waits for the operator. This load-unload time should be
balanced against the cost of one more operator.

The Rewind Time is a function of the drive only. The drive may be
speeded up in order to decrease this time. It is well to note at this time
that in the example, total cycle time is 42 minutes. Four of those
minutes were spent rewinding.

The Length of Tape Used (column 4) was used to arrive at the
Data Time (column 6). It is important to have this length measured
accurately. The Figure 68 makes the conversion between amount of
tape on the hub to the length. The measurement can be made on either

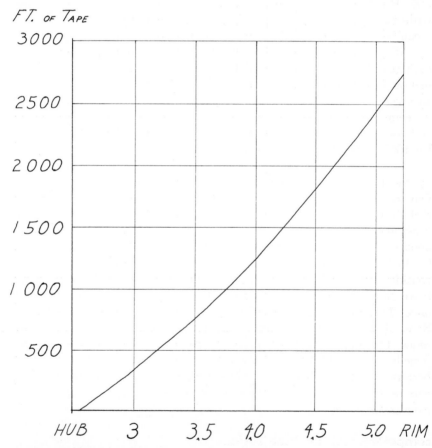

**Fig. 68**—AMOUNT OF TAPE/RADIUS OF REEL. This graph can be used to mark the reels to
estimate the amount of tape on the reel. Tape and reel tolerances can effect the measurements to some degree.

the file reel or the machine reel. If the measurement is made on the file reel, two measurements will have to be made. One at the start (assuming the reel is less than full reel), and one just before rewind. If the measurement is made on the machine reel, one measurement just before rewind will tell how much tape was used.

Length of Tape passed through the drive, times Utilization Ratio, gives the amount of tape actually recorded. The amount of tape recorded divided by the speed of the drive will tell us how much time the CPU spent reading or writing data: this is Data Time (column 6). This time is usually a good approximation. It is approximate because the computer program may write, then backspace and read. And the above formula assumes that the computer either reads or writes on a reel. However, since almost all drives have a read after write head, write backspace read is not too common. It is done so infrequently that it can be ignored. This calculation has filled in the column on Data Time.

We should be aware of the total amount of tape that is used on each reel. It is not at all unusual for programs to use up the first 100 feet on 5,000 different reels. This means that a lot of money is tied up in an inventory. If the average length of tape used is less than half a reel, it seems something should be done about the way the programming systems work. Tape is too expensive to be doled out to everyone who has 100 feet of information to store.

From Figure 67 the total of the Data Times (column 6) divided by the total time observing, multiplied by the Peak Rate, gave the Day Rate. The Day Rate tells us how fast data goes on or comes off that drive, averaged out over a working day. It most likely is a pretty gruesome figure. We have started out with a Peak Rate in the neighborhood of 15 to 120 KC or 840 KB. But we wind up with a Day Rate of 0.5 to 2 KC or 3.6 to 14.0 KB rate. There are a couple of factors to consider. First, there may be eight to ten drives on your system. Even if we have simultaneous read and write, we can only run two drives at once. Therefore, Day Rate could be, at most, 25 percent of the Peak Rate. When we start to add in the rewind, unload, and turn-around times, this figure must go below 25 percent. It is analogous to the pencils on a desk. The utilization of any one pencil is not very high because besides a black we need red, blue, and green occasionally. So true with tape drives—one drive won't do, we must be prepared and have an assortment.

## computer check on tape system

In order for the computer to keep track of the times on the tape system, the measurements that are made on the clipboard must also be made by the computer. The measurements must also be stored. The computer must have a place to store data between programs. And every program must be designed to make the measurements. If a computer is using a standard input-output program this last requirement may not be too hard.

A drum or disk would store a log for every tape drive. This log would be kept for every drive for the entire day. Three pieces of information would be entered for each entry:

1. The clock time of the entry.
2. The program number of the entry.
3. The type of long term command that was issued or terminated, the nature of the error or data on length and size of records.

Let's go down the chart in the first page of the appendix and see how a computer would handle each piece of data.

1. Load-Unload Time. This could not be separated from item 2, 7, or 10. However, the computer could keep track of the time of issuing the rewind command and the time the drive was next available. Since Rewind Time is quite predictable, Load-Unload Time and Maintenance Time are obtained by subtraction.

3. Computer Time. This time is obtained from recorded time of first availability until the rewind is given. It is elapsed clock time.

4. Length of Tape is figured from the number of records, the size of the average inter-record gaps, and density of recording.

5. Utilization Ratio is calculated from the record size used. If variable length records are used for one program, it is likely that the records should be classed less than 100 characters, less than 1,000, 1,600, 3,000, 5,000, and 10,000 characters. Of course if one record predominates in a program, this should have a category all by itself.

6. Data Time is calculated from transfer rates, length and number of records.

7. This time was covered in 1 above.

8. Is obtained by the computer and through the same process as used in the manual method of checking.

9. This was covered in # 1 above.

10. This time is read from a real time clock that is part of the computer system.

## cleanup program

After all the data on the day's work is recorded on a disk or drum, or spare tape, a cleanup program will be called to calculate and summarize the data (items 4 to 8). The program will do very much what the human did with the data he collected on a clipboard. A print-out could be made that would look very much like Figure 69. The same comments apply as in manual analysis.

## summary

This approach to computer tape drive time can be thought of as inventory control. When the computer is turned on, an inventory of time is made available to the processor. This time analysis attempts to tell where the inventory was spent or used. How can we better control the inventory?

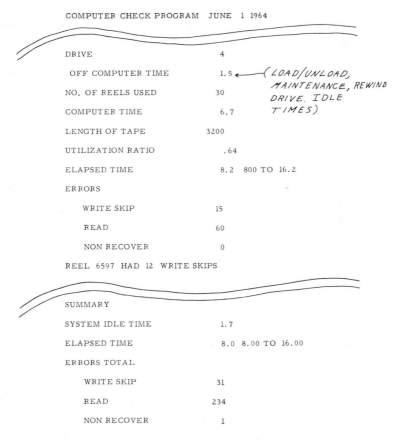

```
COMPUTER CHECK PROGRAM   JUNE  1 1964


     DRIVE                      4

        OFF COMPUTER TIME       1.5  ←—(LOAD/UNLOAD,
                                         MAINTENANCE, REWIND
        NO. OF REELS USED       30       DRIVE. IDLE
                                         TIMES)
        COMPUTER TIME           6.7

        LENGTH OF TAPE          3200

        UTILIZATION RATIO        .64

        ELAPSED TIME            8.2   800 TO  16.2

        ERRORS

            WRITE SKIP          15

            READ                60

            NON RECOVER          0

     REEL  6597  HAD  12  WRITE SKIPS


     SUMMARY

     SYSTEM IDLE TIME           1.7

     ELAPSED TIME               8.0  8.00 TO  16.00

     ERRORS TOTAL

         WRITE SKIP             31

         READ                   234

         NON RECOVER            1
```

**Fig. 69—COMPUTER PRINT OUT.** This is the type of print out that a computer check program could produce. Such total and automatic system analysis could go a long way towards improving efficiency.

# index

**159**